SOPRINTENDENZA ARCHEOLOG

# UNPEELING
# POMPEII

## STUDIES IN REGION I
## OF POMPEII

edited by
Joanne Berry

ELECTA

Catalogue of
the exhibition
in the Auditorium
of Pompeii
1st October -
8th December 1998

*Cover: Marble table and
cistern-head during the
excavation of the House
of Ceres (I.9.13).
Top reconstruction of the
decoration from the 'blue
room' in the House of the
Fruit Orchard.*

**Archaeological
Superintendency of Pompeii**
*Co-ordinators*
Antonio D'Ambrosio,
Antonio Varone
*Archaeological consultant*
Salvatore Ciro Nappo
*Architect*
Vittorio Celentano
*Archaeological documentation*
Federica Dentamaro, Rosaria
Esposito, Gennaro Iovino,
Alessandra Meneghini, Rossella
Pace, Ida Scafa, Rosaria Visone
*Computerisation*
Walter Balzano,
Antonella Dattolo

**Archaeological
Superintendency
of Naples and Caserta**
*Director*
Maria Rosaria Borriello
*Study of the finds*
Eleonora Ferrara

**University of Leiden/Dutch
Institute at Rome**
*Director*
Herman Geertman
*Computer recording*
Hans Knikman
*Archaeological documentation*
Natasja Rabouw, Cathérine
Saliou, Astrid Schoonhoven.

**Spanish Institute of Historical
Heritage (MEC)/Spanish
School of History and
Archaeology at Rome**
*Director*
Antonio Mostalac Carrillo
*Co-Directors*
José Luis Jiménez Salvador,
C. Miguel Beltran Lloris
*Wall-Paintings and Floors*
Carmen Guiral Pelegrin
*Pottery*
María Angeles Sánchez Sánchez

*Metal Objects*
Romana Erice Lacabe
*Documentation*
Paloma García
*Restoration*
Maria Antonia Moreno
Cifuentes
*Archaeological drawings*
Elvira González De Durana
*Collaborators*
Pilar Balbas, Maria Jesús
Castellanos, Teresa De La Osa,
José Juan Domingo, Peña
Lanzarote, Belén Patón, Carlos
Sáenz, Inmaculada Soriano

**The British School at Rome**
*Director*
Andrew Wallace-Hadrill
*Director of Excavations*
Michael Fulford
*Study of finds*
Joanne Berry
*Archaeological recording*
Sophie Hay, Christina Trier
*Computer recording*
Raphael Helman,
Marie-Noelle Janssens,
Justin Snell
*Reconstruction of wall decoration*
Nicholas Wood
*Exhibition*
Brigitte Desrochers
*Collaborators:* Nowal Alshaikley,
Nick Barnes, Amanda Clark,
Gill Clark, Will Clarke, Robert
Daniels-Dwyer, Janet DeLaine,
Jason Helman, Tom Jones,
Nigel Pollard, Mark Robinson,
Anthony Sibthorpe, Jane Timby,
and the many students from
the University of Reading
Department of Archaeology
who took part in seasons
of recording and excavation
between 1995 and 1998,
and student participants
in the Fieldwork Summer
School of 1997.

© 1998 Ministero per i Beni Culturali e Ambientali
Soprintendenza Archeologica di Pompei
Published by Electa, Milan
Elemond Editori Associati

*Pompeii is the richest of all archaeological sites from the ancient world. The catastrophe of volcanic eruption is a destructive force greater even than the nuclear bomb. But once the work of destruction is complete, the volcanic pumice preserves. In unpeeling the layers of pumice from the site, the archaeologist also unwittingly destroys, exposing what has survived for two thousand years to the destructive force of other, everyday, elements: rain, sun, wind, dust, and the passing feet of visitors. Pompeii has never been so much at risk of a second destruction. This exhibition comes out of a project of international collaboration by scholars concerned by this threat to Pompeii, convinced of the importance of recording, studying and interpreting the precious evidence that has already been exposed before it crumbles. The speed and carelessness of the excavations of the past now seem horrifying. We may be less surprised that areas excavated over 150 years ago, like the House of the Lyre-Player, are now in ruins; more worrying is the way that material excavated less than 50 years ago, after the second world war, like Insulae 8 and 9 of Region I, are now in a critical condition, and still await publication. Six teams from four different European countries united their efforts for the purpose of this project, encouraged by finance from the European Union. Region I, along the Via dell'Abbondanza, was chosen as focus for the project, though similar challenges and results might be found in any part of the 66 hectare site. The Superintendency of Pompeii undertook to study and restore the vast House of the Lyre-Player (I.4), while the Superintendency of Naples and Caserta, which holds the magnificent statues and other objects found in this house by the nineteenth-century excavators, undertook to study and restore them at the same time. Two teams of foreign archaeologists were, by coincidence, working in neighbouring insulae further down the road: the Spanish in Insula 8, the British in Insula 9. Both were concerned to use the techniques of modern scientific archaeology to achieve a far fuller knowledge of already excavated areas. Simultaneously, the Dutch team studying patterns of layout of roads and insulae and houses within them focused its efforts on the same area to provide an overall framework to three isolated studies. Finally, it was agreed by all participants that the massive data, that would emerge from minute study and recording of such a substantial area, could only be managed by the most up-to-date information technology: the computer experts from the University of Salerno assisted the five other teams to input their data in a common format.*

*This exhibition takes place at three levels. The first is that of a conventional exhibition set up in the Auditorium of Pompeii. Here we have tried to show what methods the modern archaeologist uses to recover and understand the traces of the past, and to build up a picture of the history and life of the city as it emerges from our project in Region I. The second level exists in 'cyberspace': the materials gathered by the partners will be available not only on computer terminals in the Auditorium, but simultaneously accessible worldwide on the computer network. The third level is in the houses themselves: the visitor may go round a selection of the houses studied and see at first hand the results of the project. Our project is only an experiment, a sample of what can be, and still needs to be done all over Pompeii and Herculaneum, and the many villas covered by the eruption. The costs of such research are daunting, and we express profound gratitude to those who have financed the work both of the group, and of individual teams: to the 'Raphael' initiative of the European Commission which provided common funding to Enterprise Oil Italiana Spa and the British Academy, that financed the British team, and to the Instituto del Patrimonio Histórico Español (MEC) which financed the Spanish team.*

Pietro Giovanni Guzzo
*Archaeological Superintendent of Pompeii*

Stefano De Caro
*Archaeological Superintendent of Naples and Caserta*

Herman Geertman
*Director of the Dutch Institute at Rome*

Antonio Mostalac Carrillo
*Head of the Heritage Unit, Zaragoza*

Andrew Wallace-Hadrill *(Co-ordinator)*
*Director of the British School at Rome*

# DEVELOPMENT OF
# THE EXCAVATIONS OF POMPEII

| | |
|---|---|
| FIRST POINT OF EXCAVATION | |
| 1748-1798 | |
| 1806-1815 | |
| 1815-1860 | |
| 1860-1879 | |
| 1879-1923 | |
| 1924-1961 | |
| 1961-1998 | |

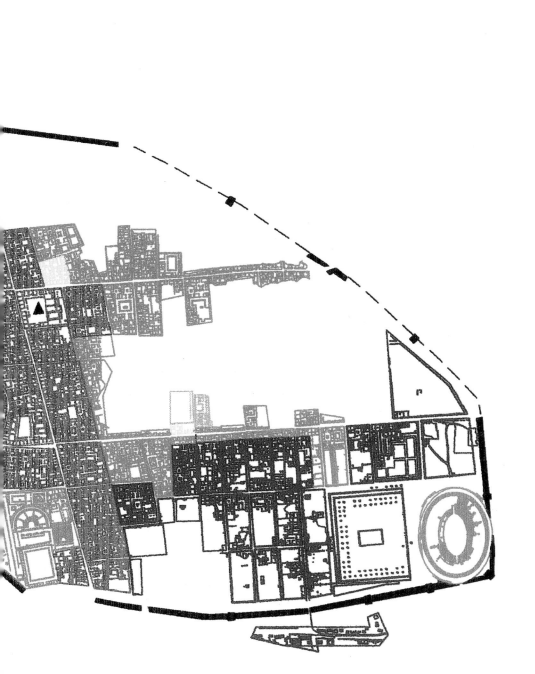

# METHODS OF ARCHAEOLOGICAL STUDY
## HISTORY OF EXCAVATION. REGION I: FIORELLI, SPINAZZOLA, MAIURI AND BEYOND

Pompeii is the oldest archaeological site in the world and as such has had a pioneering influence in the discipline of archaeology. However, the excavation which takes place in Pompeii today is very different to the activities which took place in the past. The first excavations consisted of treasure-hunting to fill the palaces and museums of Europe; until 1763 when the discovery of an inscription firmly identified the ruins as the ancient town of Pompeii, the excavated areas were back-filled and their location was generally not recorded. It is also telling that the few excavation reports from this initial period consist merely of inventories of valuable finds.

The history of the excavations is a history of changes and developments in technique and motivation, many of which correspond to changes in both political situation and the men in charge. Nowhere are these differences better illustrated than in the excavation of Region I.

By the time of the unification of Italy in 1860, more than 22 hectares or one-third of the site had been uncovered. Yet systematic excavation of Pompeii, coinciding with Pompeii's new status as a show-case of the new kingdom, only began for the first time in 1860 when Giuseppe Fiorelli became Superintendent. Fiorelli intended to finish the excavation of the town, but despite a force of between 100 - 700 workmen, this proved an impossible task. Instead he cleared the areas left between the old excava-

tions (particularly in the north-west of the town - in itself a huge task) and removed old spoil heaps. Fiorelli's impact on Pompeii was profound; however, although his aim was to recreate a unified urban whole, wall-paintings and valuable artefacts were still transported to the Naples Museum. This is what happened to the bronze statues and elaborate wall-paintings of the House of the Lyre-Player (I.4) which was excavated between 1853 and 1869 under the direction of Sangiorgio Spinelli. In addition, Fiorelli made no efforts to repair or restore the excavated buildings, claiming an 'excess' of respect for the town; the task of halting the decay of the newly exposed town was passed to his successors.

Fiorelli was called to Rome in 1875 and no more work took place in Region I until 1910, when Vittorio Spinazzola became director. Excavations in the north of the city were abandoned, and a new campaign of excavations started, along with a new method of excavation, along the Via dell'Abbondanza (of which only a small part had been uncovered) in order to connect the amphitheatre (one of the first parts of the town to have been excavated) with the rest of the city. His excavations were designed specifically to reconstruct as fully as possible the façades of the houses, with a particular emphasis on the reconstruction of the upper floors (with their windows, balconies, roofs), an element which had previously been neglected. Excavations thus proceeded horizontally, level by level, in order to record carefully the remains of the house façades, which were restored as they were excavated. It was during this period that the façades and shops of Insulae 8 and 9 in Region I were uncovered and restored. Although the work of Spinazzola gave a different face to Pompeii, the dominating figure in Italian archaeology in the twentieth century was Amedeo Maiuri. Maiuri became superintendent on 1st September 1924 and held

*1. Detail of
a wall-painting
from the House of the
Fruit Orchard (I.9.5)*

this post for a period of thirty-eight years, until 1962. His work in Pompeii must be placed in the context of Fascism and the growth of nationalistic feeling in Italy. As in the period of Italian unification, Pompeii was a source of national pride, and with the appointment of Maiuri excavations were intensified. Work took place particularly along the south side of the Via dell'Abbondanza, in Regions I and II, and aimed, in Maiuri's own words, to give a vision of one of the most interesting quarters of the town. The period until the Second World War included his two greatest discoveries: the Villa of the Mysteries and the House of the Menander (I.10.4). Insula 8 was excavated from 1936-41, and the excavation of Insulae 6, 7, and 10 in Region I were also completed. Stratigraphic excavations also took place under the AD79 levels in various parts of the town, including in the Forum, Triangular Forum, the House of the Surgeon, and Maiuri repeatedly stressed the importance of such investigations for the understanding of the history and development of the town. Restorations of all excavated buildings (not just the exceptional ones as previously) were

also given a much greater importance during this period. World World 2 stopped all work at Pompeii, and the site was bombed by the Allies during 1943.

After the war, excavations were started again as part of a campaign of public works: construction companies provided a workforce in return for the excavated lapilli, which was used in the construction of the motorway from Naples to Salerno. In order to provide the necessary lapilli, the excavations restarted in Region I at a headlong pace, sometimes with up to 100 men working in the same area, so that almost the entire area was finished in the space of ten years. The excavation of the House of Ceres (I.9.13), for example, took a mere three months in 1951. It is clear that gardens and open areas were targeted in this period, since these areas yielded the greatest amount of lapilli. Consequently the excavation of many small rooms and corners were left unfinished. The result is that the records of these excavations are in the main extremely bad and completely unpublished. Most of the excavation of Insula 9 was completed in 1951-1952.

Since the retirement of Maiuri in 1962, large-scale excavation has slowed down at Pompeii in favour of limited, carefully documented excavation and conservation. The discovery of the House of Fabius Rufus, the House of Julius Polybius and the House of the Chaste Lovers are all examples of recently and meticulously excavated houses. However, the focus of the most recent excavations at Pompeii has been to investigate the earlier levels of the structures already uncovered by past excavations and typically left unpublished.

The main focus of excavation at Pompeii in all periods has been to uncover the houses and other buildings which existed in AD79, to illustrate life in a Roman town in a particular moment of its history, and the quality of such excavations has improved drastically since the earliest days of treasure-hunting. It is impor-

*2. Excavations along the Via dell'Abbondanza in the 1910s*

*3. Excavations in the House of Successus (I.9.3) in 1952*

tant to note that excavations designed to uncover earlier structures and phases in the history of Pompeii have taken place in different periods, but it is only very recently that scholars have systematically sought to use a variety of modern archaeological techniques to understand better the historical development of the town. The following chapters illustrate some of the approaches which are being pursued today and demonstrate the importance of combining the study of the structures which existed in AD79 with stratigraphic excavation beneath these structures.

[J.B.]

*4. British archaeologists
at work in the 1990s*

*5. Spanish archaeologists
at work in the 1990s*

# STRATIGRAPHIC EXCAVATION
## EXCAVATION BELOW THE LAPILLI

The principal objective of past excavation in Pompeii has been to remove the blanket of volcanic ash and lapilli to reveal the remains of the city as it was at the time of the eruption in AD79. The extraordinary preservation of buildings with their frescoes and pavements has severely limited the opportunities for investigating the history of the city, but the survival of the city wall, for example, is a constant, visual reminder of the great antiquity of the city. While much can be learnt of relative change through time from the exacting study of the structures which survive above ground level, it is much more difficult either to define an absolute chronology of those developments, or to begin to determine changing use of space through time.

Stratigraphic excavation involves the careful removal of the different layers of soil which underlie the ground surface of AD79. In recognising the characteristics which distinguish one layer from another it follows that it is possible to differentiate the artefacts and ecofacts from each layer so that changes through time can be established. Recognition of datable objects such as coins or distinctive types of pottery will enable a chronology to be established for the sequence of excavated layers. Where layers can be associated with the construction trenches and foundations of individual walls it should be possible to establish dates from the associated material finds. Most of the excavation is carried out by hand using small, builders' pointing-trowels.

In addition, the finer sieving of samples of soil enables the recovery of very small items, such as charred seeds, bird-, or fish-bones. Such samples complement the retrieval by hand of pottery sherds, animal bone, coins and other small objects of metal or glass, building materials, etc, etc. Altogether the full range of artefacts and environmental data will enable a reconstruction at a general level of changing economy and diet. When we can be certain that our finds relate specifically to our houses, it is possible to say something of their function and the lifestyle of the inhabitants. So the biological contents of latrine and other rubbish pits will inform us directly of the diet and occupation of the inhabitants, whereas the contents of layers laid down to provide a level floor-surface within the house may have been drawn from elsewhere in the town.

[M.G.F.]

## Chronology of ceramics

| Date | Ceramic | Characteristics |
| --- | --- | --- |
| End of c. 1BC - c. 2AD | Terra sigillata | Produced in Italy, South Gaul and the East, this ceramic has a characteristic red/orange/brown glaze and a fine clay. Plain and decorated versions exist, and the marks of the manufacturer were often stamped on the bottom of the vessels. |
| c. 3BC - c. 1AD | Thin-walled wares | Produced in Central Italy, this ceramic has a well-baked clay generally less than 3mm in thickness, varying from beige to a red-brown in colour, and sometimes decorated with appliques. |
| End of c. 3 - first half of c. 1BC | Campanian black glaze | Produced in Campania, this ceramic has a coarse red-brown clay with a bright black glaze; decoration may be stamped or incised. |
| c. 7 - c. 5BC | Bucchero | Ceramic produced in Etruria which is black both on the inside and outside with a shiny surface. |
| c. 7 - c. 4BC | Greek imports | Imported from Corinth and Athens (black and red figure vessels). |

*6-10. Clockwise from top left: terra sigillata, thin-walled wares, bucchero, Greek imports, Campanian black glaze*

# UNPEELING POMPEII
## AREAS TO BE VISITED

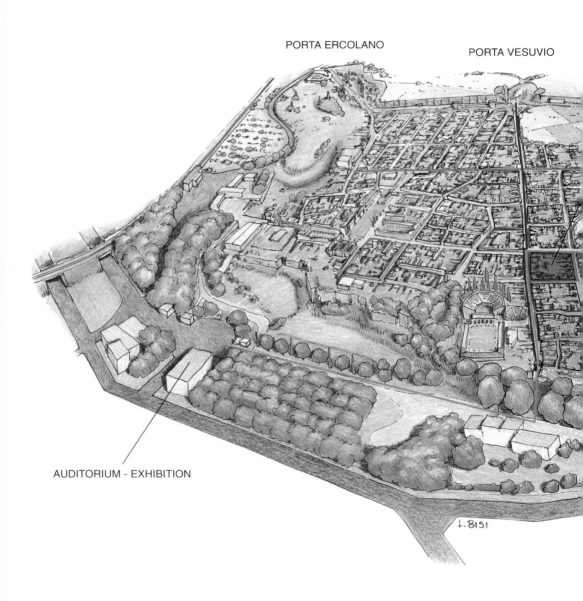

PORTA ERCOLANO

PORTA VESUVIO

AUDITORIUM - EXHIBITION

1.BISI

ITINERARY OF THE VISIT

VIA DI STABIA

VIA DI NOLA

VIA DELL'ABBONDANZA

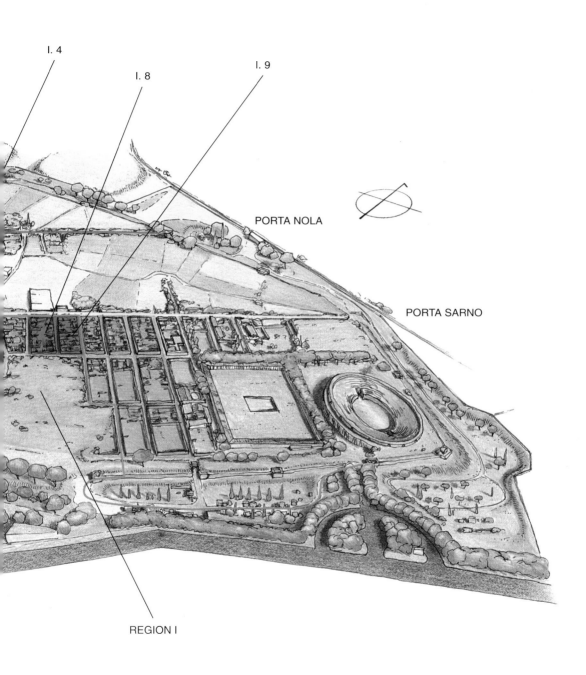

I. 4

I. 8

I. 9

PORTA NOLA

PORTA SARNO

REGION I

# THE LAYOUT OF THE CITY AND ITS HISTORY
# THE DUTCH PROJECT

In 1858, to aid the administration of the site, the ancient town of Pompeii was divided into nine regions. As can be seen in Region I, this modern division is not connected to the ancient urban structure and its history: instead, Region I consists of a collection of *insulae* which belong to two different ancient quarters of the town and to two different phases of urban development.

The subject of our research is the extension of the town outside the ancient core of Pompeii. Such extension meant the creation both of a new network of streets and new quarters. The research starts from several premises:

- the urban expansion had a systematic character and this was decided by public authorities;

- given the several notable differences between the new quarters, they developed over time rather than in one period. In other words, the urban context which we see today is considered to be the result of one or more regulated plans. We maintain that such plans are identifiable through the analysis of metrological phenomena and through observations concerning topography and construction.

To date, three levels of data have been gathered. The first level concerns the layout of the principal streets, the position of the gates of the city and the development of both in the surrounding territory; the second level concerns the individual quarters and their articulation; the third level concerns the original partition of each *insula* and its first (that is, the oldest recognisable) construction.

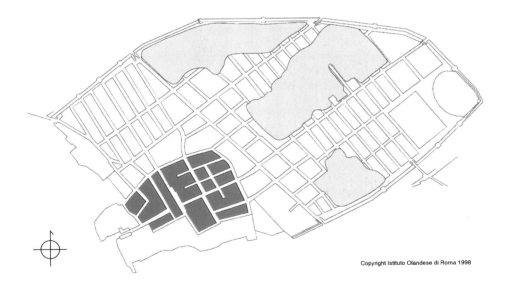

*11. Aerial photograph of part of Region I*

*12. The grey areas represent the unexcavated areas of the site; the first phase of development of the town is indicated in red*

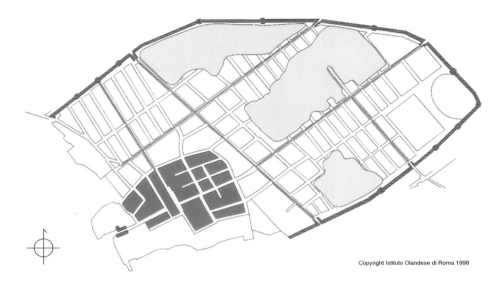

## The site and the first town

The origins of Pompeii date back to the archaic period when, sometime between the eight and sixth centuries BC, an urban nucleus grew up in connection with two sanctuaries, one to Apollo and the other to Minerva or Hercules. The settlement was located on the promontory of a high lava plateau near to the mouth of the river Sarno. Only certain elements of this original nucleus were conserved in the later Roman town buried by Vesuvius in AD79; today these can be seen in the irregular plan of the south-west zone of the town which clearly contrasts with the regular expansion of the new zones which were added later.

## Walls, gates and street networks

In the second half of the sixth century BC the indigenous Oscan population decided to build a fortification wall around a wide area to the north-east of the urban nucleus, which offered protection to agricultural activities and to herds. The motive for this may have been to provide protection from Greek or Etruscan expansion, or it may have been due to internal tensions between the indigenous populations of the region. The course of these walls seems to have remained unchanged in the following centuries.

The network of streets which structured the new urban area was formed from five axes, two going from east to west, and three from north to south. The position and orientation of the principle north-south axis is dictated by the layout of the terrain, while the orientation of the east-west axis follows altrimetric lines. The principal north-south axis, the Via Stabiana and its continuation on the Via Vesuvio, was divided into three equal parts which fixed the exact position of the transversal axes. Of these, that to the north, from the crossroads with the Via Consolare to the Porta di Nola, has the same length as the Via Stabiana between the two gates, while half of this length is found in the tract of the

*13. The grey areas represent the unexcavated areas of the site; the plan highlights the principal network of streets*

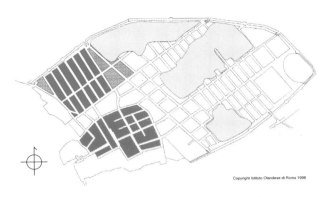

Copyright Istituto Olandese di Roma 1998

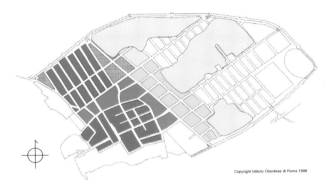

Copyright Istituto Olandese di Roma 1998

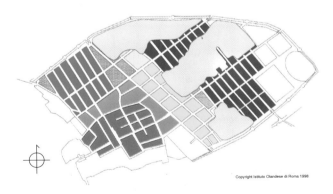

Copyright Istituto Olandese di Roma 1998

south axis which connects the Via Stabiana with the Via di Nocera. The regular position and calculation of the principal roads makes it clear that this grid was the result of an act of planning by the city authorities.

In contrast, it is uncertain if the area reserved for agricultural activities and scattered homes originally followed this subdivision or whether the grid was created after a partial or complete building up of the area within the walls. The position of the five gates in the city wall is dictated by the network of streets, but it is surprising that none of these gates is really on axis with the street network. This leads to the conclusion that the gates and the network of streets were not the result of a single project but rather of a kind of compromise between two separate plans. It seems likely that the first plan saw the construction of a fortification wall, the positioning of the gates, and a regular division of the area inside the walls. When, at a later date, proper streets were laid down, the existing situation was taken as a point of departure.

## The expansion of the built-up area

Between the fourth and third centuries BC, in the Samnite period, or perhaps between the third and the second cen-

*14-16. The grey areas represent the unexcavated areas of the site; in the first plan green indicates the second phase of urban development; in the second plan, yellow indicates the third phase and orange the fourth phase of development; in the third plan, blue indicates the last quarter to be developed*

tury BC when Campania was increasingly influenced by the newly emerging power of Rome, the existing built-up area of the town was expanded by the addition of new quarters. This expansion had a systematic character and was the result of one or more regulated plans undertaken in phases. Three different systems of division and orientation can be identified: the north-west zone which has the Via di Mercurio as its axis whose orientation is determined by the Forum; the zone of the squared *insulae*, whose orientation has been determined by the north-south axis of the Via Stabiana, and finally the east zone which has the Via di Nocera as its axis and perpendicularly the Via di Nola and the Via dell'Abbondanza.

Between these three zones there are two areas where the shape of the *insulae* is irregular because they fill in the gaps between quarters of different orientations. Examination of how the three main zones were connected to each other offers the possibility of establishing a relative chronology for their layout and excludes the possibility that they were contemporary, even if they were all laid out over a short time-span.

The first plan comprised the two zones immediately to the north and east of the old city. For a certain period the boundaries of the built-up area of the city were defined by the east side of the squared *insulae*. Close study of how these two zones connect suggests that the oldest extension was that in the north-west quarter. Then twelve *insulae* in the form of parallelograms were planned on the two sides of the Via di Mercurio. Later, to the east of these, four *insulae* were added along the Via di Vesuvio.

In a second phase, a double series of *insulae* was planned to the east of the old city, whose square form was determined by the strong north-south slope of the ground. The zone became connected with the north-west quarter by the addition of two *insulae*, with the effect that the two new quarters formed a belt around the old city.

The creation of this new situation led to the building-up of the area immediately outside the old city and the two new quarters. The fact that the streets here are not straight demonstrates that older streets already existed here and that the building was not conducted as part of a regular plan.

This situation, of a built-up area to the west and an open area to the east, existed for a certain period before building was allowed in the eastern zone too. For the moment it is uncertain when this occurred, but it was perhaps in the late third century BC or the second century BC. The new quarter was connected to the already existing zones of the town by the insertion of a series of *insulae* of irregular form. The same quarter also had *insulae* of a regular rectangular form and streets which intersected them at right angles. Presumably this whole area to the east was destined to be covered by *insulae*, but later, in the first century BC, parts gave way to the amphitheatre and other particular buildings.

The 120 or more *insulae* of Pompeii are not individual blocks separated by a network of streets. Rather one must think of groups of *insulae* and streets in zones which were constructed in a predetermined spatial and chronological order and which, surrounded by the principal street network, continued to function as quarters.

## The division of the individual *insulae*

When attempting to identify original partition of each *insula*, we seek to define both the technical criteria which were adopted by the surveyors of the land, and the social and economic criteria which guided the municipal authority in the partition of lots and the buyers in their choice of future property. At first sight, this seems a hard task. Buildings have often been restructured, divided into different properties, or joined with other properties to form a single large complex. The traces of many of these changes can be seen in the façades of the *insulae*.

## Methodology

The aspects to be considered are building, metrological and judicial phenomena.

The materials and the techniques of construction of the façades of the *insulae* and, where necessary, the situation inside the buildings are examined. Observations are recorded on formulaic notes which codify the phenomena.

At the same time as the analysis of the walls, the façade of the *insula* is measured from corner to corner in order to record the exact position of the observed phenomena. The basis of this detailed analysis is formed by reliefs drawn during our first season of work with the help

# History of the city

Pompeii's position linked it to the changing historical circumstances of the Bay of Naples. Divided from the north of the Bay and the northern Campanian plain by Vesuvius, it stands at the outlet of the valley of the Sarno river, and is linked by the river to the mountains of the hinterland.

*Iron Age (c. 10-8BC).* There was probably a prehistoric settlement at Pompeii, but though iron age burials are common in the surrounding area (e.g. at Striano), scarcely any evidence has been found in Pompeii.

*Greek-Etruscan.* The eighth - sixth centuries BC were marked in the area by two rival colonising movements. Greek settlers established cities on the coast, especially to the north of the Bay of Naples. Etruscans from central Italy either settled, or economically dominated, sites in the interior and south of Vesuvius from Capua to Salerno. Pompeii fell in the Etruscan sphere. Already by 600BC the entire present circuit of the city was fortified. Two major cult sites belong to this phase, the temple of Apollo in the Forum, and the sanctuary, probably of Minerva and Hercules, in the Triangular Forum.

*Samnite.* During the fifth century BC, the local population, whom the Romans called 'Samnites', took control of many Greek cities (including Cumae), and many Etruscan ones (including Capua). The local Italic dialect of Oscan was spoken. Until c. 200BC, the city seems to have had little economic significance, and few traces of this period survive, except for the fortifications which reflect wars and instability.

*Roman-Samnite.* Pompeii already passed under Roman control during the conquest of southern Italy in the late fourth and early third centuries BC. It retained independence as an 'allied' city, supplying ships or troops. After the defeat of Hannibal, Pompeii as an ally shared in Rome's wars of Mediterranean conquest. Economically, it experienced a boom reflected in building all over the city, including the magnificent palace of the House of the Faun.

In 90BC, Pompeii joined the many allied cities of Italy which rebelled against Rome to demand full citizenship. It was stormed by the dictator Sulla in 89BC, and was resettled as a Roman colony.

*Roman.* The colony (named *Colonia Cornelia Veneria Pompeianorum*), founded by the dictator's nephew in 80BC, combined previous Samnite inhabitants and new Roman settlers. All were Roman citizens, living under Roman law. Latin was the official language, and the city government, under annually elected magistrates and a council, followed a standard Roman model. Many new public buildings, including amphitheatre, small theatre, and temples of Venus and of Jupiter, mark the new city.

The prosperity of the second century increased with the peace and Mediterranean-wide trade brought by the first emperor, Augustus. A riot in the amphitheatre (AD59) followed by a serious earthquake (AD62/3) turned the city's fortunes. Despite massive rebuilding, the eruption of AD79 found the city still damaged by this and subsequent earthquakes. [A.W.H.]

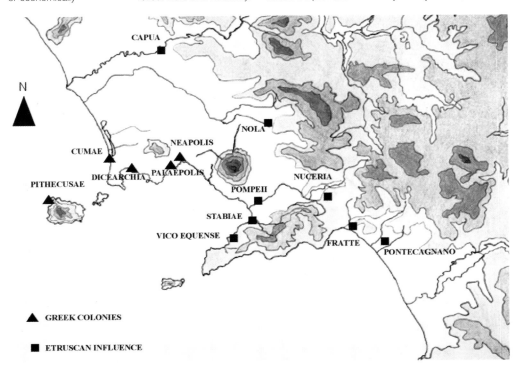

▲ **GREEK COLONIES**

■ **ETRUSCAN INFLUENCE**

of the Faculty of Geodesy of the Polytechnic of Delft.

Metrological analysis is performed by converting the metric data into Oscan feet. In the greater part of cases, one finds systematic sequences of division in the *insulae* which are difficult to interpret as casual.

Concerning the judicial aspect of our study, we have noted amongst other things that the pavements display variations in their surface and in the make-up of their borders which often coincide with the limits of a property. Evidently individual owners had the obligation to construct and maintain the pavement. This, and other similar phenomena, are indications of the original division of properties which otherwise are unrecognisable.

## The *Insula* of the Menander (I.10)

*Insula* I.10 forms part of the group of squared *insulae* along the Via Stabiana, although due to the layout of the principal streets it is more

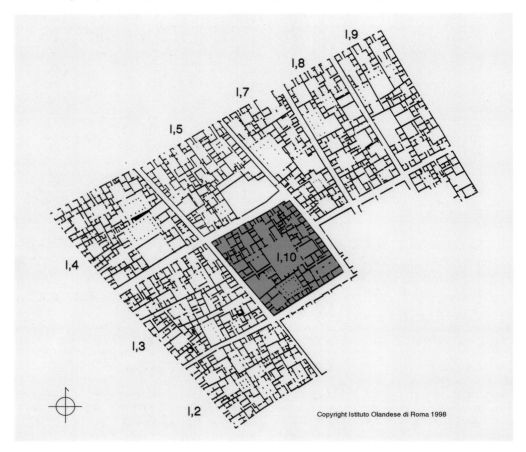

Copyright Istituto Olandese di Roma 1998

*17. Plan of Region I,
highlighting the position
of Insula I.10*

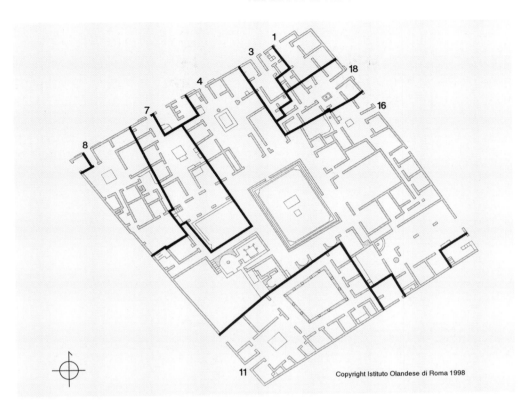

Copyright Istituto Olandese di Roma 1998

accurate to describe their shapes as parallelograms. The lengths of the *insulae* vary from 190 to 225 Oscan feet (an Oscan foot measures around 27,55cm and is divided into twelve digits). In most of the *insulae* it is possible to identify a general division of the surface-area into two or three units which then have been subdivided into single lots. In the case of Insula I.10, the original division of the surface-area into two or three

units was extensively disturbed by the expansion of the House of the Menander (I.10.4). This expansion profoundly changed the appearance and spatial articulation of the *insula*. Despite this, a certain number of phenomena remain recognisable and allow us to arrive at both a general and, in part, a detailed reconstruction of the original subdivision of the *insula*. Moreover, it can be seen that some of these phenomena are connected to the oldest methods of construction found in the city (*opus quadratum, opus Africanum*, and *opus incertum* connected to these).
The boundaries of the properties, as they existed in AD79, are indicated in the plan above. Two houses of average size to the north-west, a similar house to the south-west,

and three small houses to the north-east cover less than a half of the surface-area of the *insula*. The house of the Menander extends over the remaining area.
The original layout of the *insula* can be more easily seen on the north façade of the *insula*. Here one finds five lots which were built in order from east to west. In the first stretch of 120 feet, three houses can be seen, of which the first two, as indicated by the position of the dividing wall and its connection with the façade, seem to have been built at the same time.
To the north-west corner, a stretch of 85 feet comprised two lots. As can be seen from several phenomena in the construction and orientation of the dividing wall between the two houses, the last house

*18. Division of properties in Insula I.10 in AD79*

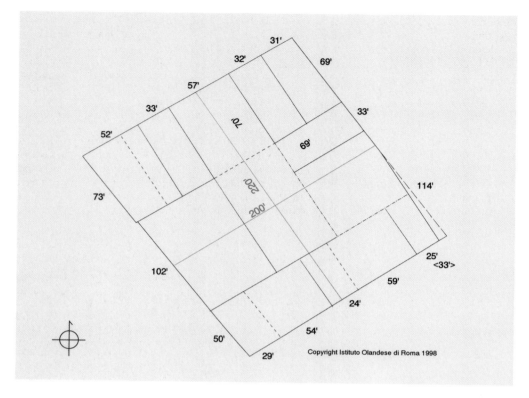

*19. Original layout of the Insula I.10*

to have been built was the one on the corner.

All five of the houses have a north-south orientation. A line of 70 feet between the façades formed the rear limit of the houses. It seems that only the House of the Menander extended beyond this line with a deep garden. The two smallest houses towards the north-east corner were restructured later which created a third house with its entrance on the east façade of the *insu-la* (house 18), but originally even these two had a depth of 70 feet.

On the east façade a very ancient house has an east-west orientation (house 16). Beyond this, the expansion of the House of the Menander has cancelled all traces of the original plan.

On the west façade a similar situation can be seen. The façade lateral to the house at the north-west corner, which is more than 70 feet in length, follows a tract of around 150 feet to the south-west corner. This tract is divided into a first part of little more than 100 feet which belongs to the House of the Menander, and the façade of a house (house 11) which has a length of around 50 feet and occupies the south-west part of the *insula*.

Examination of the south façade reveals that this last house was not part of the original construction of the *insula*. In fact, the remains of the façade of an earlier house are recognisable in the wall lateral to the house. This façade is constructed in *opus Africanum*, with an entrance (fauces) 6,66 feet wide (80 digits) and tracts of wall to both sides of the entrance 23,66 wide. To the right of this façade follows another tract of 23,66 feet, built in different materials and perhaps originally open. Immediately after this the remains of a corner can be seen, the only element conserved of a house which extended beyond it. At a distance of 25 feet from the south-east corner the perimeter wall of the *insula* curves slightly; this too can be connected to the previous situation.

By putting together this and

other data, the oldest recognisable division of the *insula* can be described as follows. The *insula* has the shape of an irregular parallelogram. The north-south axis is 220 feet, the east-west axis is 200 feet. The *insula* was articulated in three zones. Those to the north and south had lots with a north-south orientation; in the central one the orientation was east-west. The 'circular' design which resulted from this way of planning the lots created a central space which could have been exploited in many ways. In the case of this *insula*, it seems that from the beginning a part of this central space functioned as the garden of the House of the Menander. This house, situated at the centre of the most important façade, was the widest of the *insula* (60 of a maximum 160 feet). The other houses were divided into two groups of small lots, which in at least three cases became lots of average size by combining the two formats. During the original construction of Insula 10, therefore, houses belonging to three economic levels were planned or subsequently created. A rigidly unitary division is clearly absent. The reconstructed scheme of land-division, which was adapted to the physical needs of the place and to the personal needs of the first owners and builders of the lots, can be seen in the plan below. [H.G.]

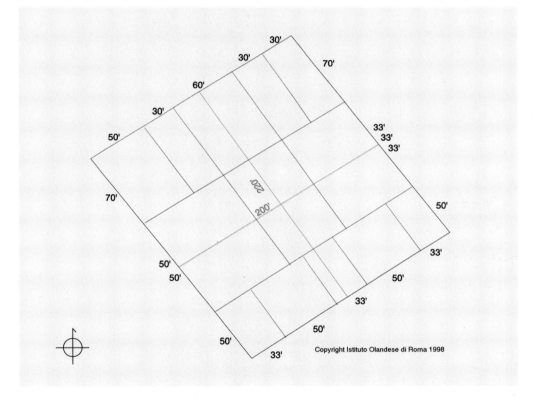

Copyright Istituto Olandese di Roma 1998

*20. Original scheme of land-division of Insula I.10*

# INSULA I.4 AND THE HOUSE OF THE LYRE-PLAYER
# THE ITALIAN PROJECT

For some time studies of the history and construction of Pompeii have emphasised the need to study the 'insula', that is, the urban space delineated by four streets in all its elements. *Insula* I.4. was chosen in light of its significant urban location and the fact that it contains one of the largest houses in the town. This led to the reconstruction of its construction history, its social and economic history, and the recontextualisation of its contents and decoration.

The *insula* was excavated in the period from February 1853 to February 1869, mainly under the direction of Sangiorgio Spinelli, and attracted interest due to its splendid wall and floor decoration, and the discovery of a good number of portrait heads and a splendid bronze statue of Apollo the Lyre-Player (from which the House of the Lyre-Player acquires its name). All of the contents and the large wall-paintings were stripped, and, despite the restorations which took place during the excavations, the *insula* suffered a slow but progressive decay. Above all, the location of the *insula* should have accorded it greater attention: it lies at a nerve-point of the urban network, at the crossroads of two of the most important roads of the ancient city, the Via dell'Abbondanza and the Via di Stabia. It is likely that its building history was the result of social and economic changes which took place on these roads.

The *insula* is part of the double rows of almost square *insulae* which are found to the east of the Via dell'Abbondanza. Another particular characteristic of the *insula* is its gradient: the architecture which slowly developed here always had to take into account the natural slope of the ground, which in this part of the town is much more dramatic than elsewhere and which determined the orientation and alignment of the different properties at the moment of their initial foundation. Moreover, in AD79 the *insula* contained one of the most conspicuous properties in the town, the result of a complex and long construction history. During the last few years substantial restoration has permitted greater understanding of this significant part of Pompeii.

Our project had two aims: to establish the history of the *insula*, and to reconstruct the state of affairs, for now limited to the House of the Lyre-Player, at the moment of its tragic burial. This has provided a significant insight about the economic, social and cultural state of the town in the years after the earthquake of AD62/3.

When the *insula* was originally founded in the second half of the third century BC it was divided into ten properties, of more or less the same size, and positioned according to the gradient of the terrain: three in the south-east section facing the street to the south, three in the south-west section opening onto the Via di Stabia, and four to the north opening into the Via dell'Abbondanza.

Of the first group a splendid façade in *opus quadratum* of Sarno stones, miraculously preserved today as the perimeter wall of the houses of later phases.

The boundaries of the second group are clearly visible thanks to the preservation of the original façades in *opus Africanum* and *opus quadratum*.

The third group of houses are equally identifiable, above all thanks to the internal perimeter walls, the original division; it is possible that already in the first phase the north-west corner, in correspondence

*21. Statue of Apollo the Lyre-Player, National Archaeological Museum of Naples*

with the crossroads of the Via dell'Abbondanza and the Via di Stabia which were undoubtedly important from a commercial point of view, was later subdivided into more commercial establishments. The houses in this phase therefore were smaller with rooms located around the *atrium* or uncovered courtyard, with a small garden in the rear.

A radical transformation took place when Pompeii became a Roman colony after 80BC; in particular the three houses to the south-east and the central house of the south-western part were amalgamated into one complex with an entrance on the Via dell'Abbondanza. This new house, the House of the Lyre-Player, had an unusual layout for Pompeii and for Italy in general. House 25 also expanded at the expense of the house immediately to the east.

Later, at the beginning of the first century AD, the most important element which determined the form of the *insula* and the activities of its shops to the north-west, was the location of the public fountain, placed in correspondence with the crossroads of the Via dell'Abbondanza and the Via di Stabia, which led to the withdrawal of the west façade in that point and therefore an adjustment of the boundary with house 10.

The last transformation occurred in the period between the earthquake of AD62/3 and the eruption of AD79 when the owner of the House of the Lyre-Player acquired the house at no.25; in these years a large part of the north and west façades of the *insula* were filled by shops and craft shops.

The eruption surprised the *insula* while the damage from an earthquake, which possibly had occurred only a few months before, was being repaired. It is likely that the activities in the shops and workshops of this *insula* had not yet returned to their normal rhythm. In addition, the pavement to the west and north of the *insula* had been dug up in order to install a new system of water-supply and thus access to each of the houses and shops would have been extremely difficult.

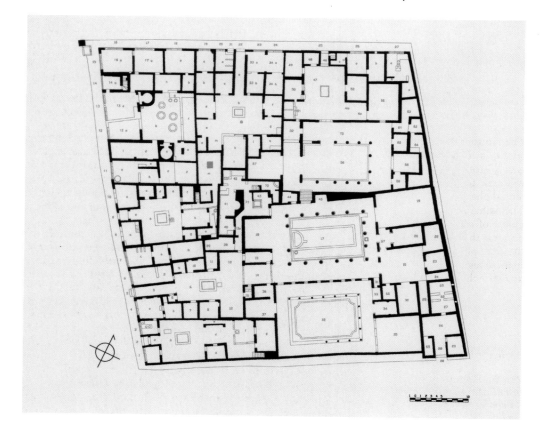

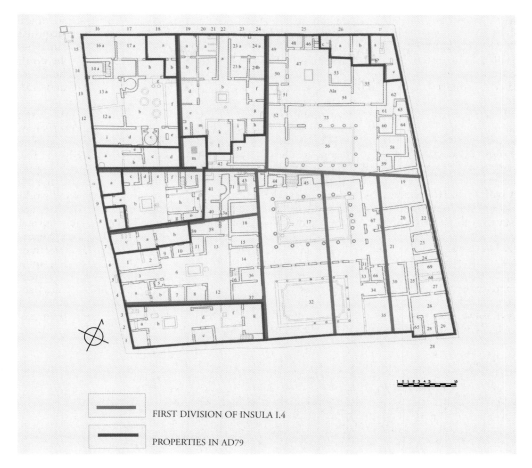

FIRST DIVISION OF INSULA I.4

PROPERTIES IN AD79

The House of the Lyre-Player reveals a complex construction history which here we will seek to outline in its essential phases.

The principal entrance to the House of the Lyre-Player is at no.5 on the Via di Stabia. In the first phase it was an extremely regular house with an *atrium* which extended to-

*22. Insula I.4. in AD79*

*23. Plan illustrating the first division of Insula I.4 and its subsequent condition in AD79*

wards the east to the change in level which separated it from the houses to the east and west (no.2 and no.9). Access to the centre of the house was achieved through a long vestibule flanked by two shops of equal size and connected to the *atrium*. The rooms around the *atrium* were laid out almost symmetrically. It is difficult to understand how the space was organised to the rear of the house, but there must have been a reception room and a garden. Pertinent to this phase is the first style wall-decoration of room 11 to the left of the *atrium*.

In the second phase, which corresponds to the acquisition

of all three properties to the east, a splendid house was created on the grounds of its size and the novelty of its architectural form. The long entrance with vestibule and fauces leads to the *atrium*, where the *impluvium* basin was moved forwards; in axis with it a large rectangular *tablinum* opened, preceded by two grand *alae*. Behind these are two large peristyles which are divided by a wall with windows positioned exactly on axis with the *tablinum* and *atrium*. At the rear there are three large reception rooms. In this phase the garden of House 9 was acquired, and the grandiose bath suite preceded by an ele-

## Analysis of standing structures

The analysis of the elements which make up a wall - the materials, their combination and the techniques of construction - allows us to trace the construction history of that wall and thus of the room and the house that it belongs to. In many cases the walls have been covered by thick layers of painted plaster, and these would often be changed during the history of a house, just as today we change wall-paper. The possibility of seeing different decorative patterns executed at different times and with different characteristics on the walls of Pompeii today allows us to have a fairly accurate picture of fashions and of the activities of painting workshops in the ancient city. Similar developments affect the pavements of individual rooms of the houses, which range from the finest mosaics in reception rooms of the wealthiest houses to simple floors of crushed ceramics in secondary rooms and in poor houses. The different construction techniques, wall-decoration and pavements of rooms, their relationships, both temporal and in fashion/taste, allow us to read more or less precisely the history of a room, of the house it belongs to, and of the insula which the house forms part of.

*Construction techniques*
Construction techniques vary according to the quality of the materials, the different combinations of these materials, and different ways of building the wall:
*Opus quadratum* at Pompeii was used above all in the city walls and in the façades of the houses; the workforce had to be skilled since the blocks would be erected without cement. Materials: dark grey pappamonte tufo. Date: 650BC onwards;
*Opus incertum* is the most common construction technique, consisting of two skins of irregularly placed stones filled with cementum, a mixture of fragments of stone and mortar. Materials: Sarno stone and dark lava basalt.

Date: c. 200BC onwards;
*Opus Africanum* consists of vertical chains of blocks of Sarno stone placed alternatively horizontally and vertically and filled with *opus incertum*. Materials: Sarno stone. Date: c.500BC on;
*Opus spicatum* was used above all to knit together walls or in pavements,

and consists of blocks of latericium placed in a fish-bone pattern. Materials: brick. Date: 1st c. BC onwards;
*Opus reticulatum* was formed by two external layers of small, square-faced blocks set in a network pattern. When the network is only approximate, it is

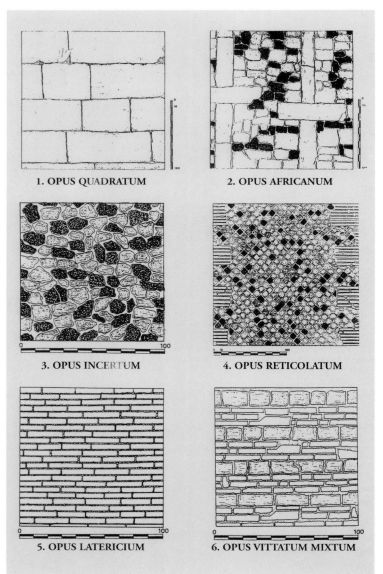

**1. OPUS QUADRATUM**

**2. OPUS AFRICANUM**

**3. OPUS INCERTUM**

**4. OPUS RETICOLATUM**

**5. OPUS LATERICIUM**

**6. OPUS VITTATUM MIXTUM**

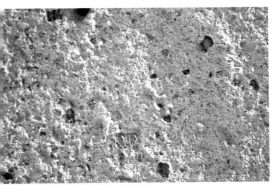
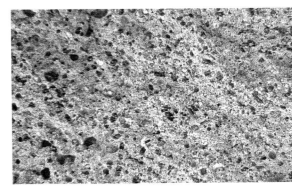

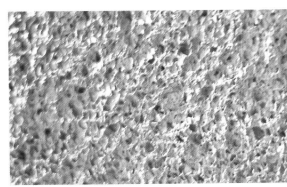

called *quasi-reticulatum*. Materials: grey tufo, Sarno stone, basalt. Date: 60BC onwards. *Opus latericium* instead used blocks of terracotta (*bipedales*) to form the external layers. Materials: terracotta tiles. Date: 60BC onwards; *Opus craticium* was used above all for partition walls and for upper floors and was constructed by a wooden framework which enclosed a single layer of *opus incertum*. Materials: grey tufo, Sarno stone, basalt. Date: end 1st c. BC onwards;

*Opus vittatum* was made from two external layers of regularly placed blocks. Materials: tufo or Sarno stone. Date: 1st c. AD onwards; *Opus vittatum mixtum* was used mainly in the period after the earthquake of AD62/3 and consisted of rows of rectangular blocks alternating with two or three rows of brick. In some cases, fragments of tile were substituted for brick. Materials: tufo, Sarno stone, bricks, broken tiles. Date: from AD35 onwards. [S.N.C.]

*24. Different construction techniques used at Pompeii*

*25-29. Clockwise from top left: yellow tufo, grey lava, lava crust, grey Nucerian tufo, Sarno stone*

gant tetrastyle *atrium* was built. Undoubtedly the form and character of this phase leads one to think of the acquirement of Hellenistic culture with the development of bold prospectives and unusual architectural foreshortenings. We do not know what led to the resizing of the large rectangular *tablinum*, perhaps structural reasons, or still more probably the desire to have a *tablinum* of the customary shape and characteristics. This occured when second style wall-painting was still in fashion, as can be seen still today in room 36 which opens off the south peristyle.

In the Augustan age, the house was adorned with expensive third style paintings, dominated by large mythological scenes such as the sleeping Antiope (room 19), Nemesis and the swan, Apollo and Poseidon and Venus and Mars (room 20). The peristyle to the left contained bronze statues,

among which was that of Apollo the Lyre-Player. The quality of life in this period is also illustrated by the grandiose bath suite consisting of *apodyterium, tepidarium, calidarium* and a small tetrastyle *atrium*. The spectacular architectural sequence, the themes of the wall-decoration, and the use of the peristyles clearly demonstrates the impact of Greek fashions at the end of the first century BC.

The events following the earthquake of AD62/3 allowed the property to extend further, incorporating the house at no.28 which was reached by the construction of a stairway in *opus latericium* (overcoming the difference in level). The continuing earthquakes meant that a good part of the wall decoration had to be redone, but high quality was always maintained: room 35 received a splendid painting with Iphigenia in Tauris and Dionysius and Ariadne, while room 21

was decorated with a grandiose Judgement of Paris.

In the final years of the city, the house appears to have had financial problems and lost its air of affluence. In fact, it was forced to cede parts of the house which became shops and upper floor rented apartments along the Via dell'Abbondanza. The baths were no longer in use and its pavement was in part ruined. The northern peristyle was reduced in size by the construction of rooms between its columns. Finally, the large *tablinum* was reduced in size, so much so that whoever passed along the Via di Stabia no longer had an impression of large spaces and marvellous gardens.

From the point of view of an absolute chronology, it is proposed that the first phase occurred in the second half of the third century BC, while there is good reason to suppose that the successive phase can be connected to the trans-

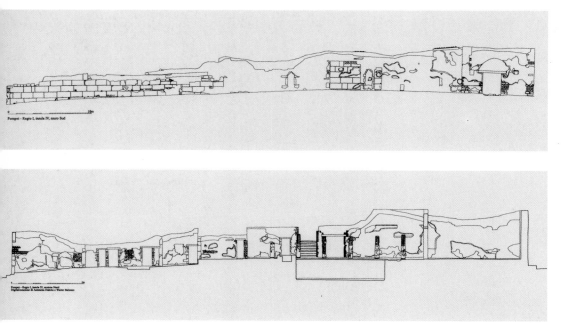

Pompei - Regio I, insula IV, muro Sud

Pompei - Regio I, insula IV, sezione Nord
Digitalizzazione di Antonino Daniele e Walter Belisano

formation of Pompeii into a colony (80BC). The third phase is ascribable to the last years of the first century BC when most of the house was decorated in third style wall-painting. The events between the earthquake of AD62/3 and the eruption of AD79 determined the last transformations. However, it is clear that small changes would have oc-

*30. The south façade of the insula, illustrating the traces of its original division*

*31. West-east section of the House of the Lyre-Player*

*32. The lower peristyle (32) of the House of the Lyre-Player*

curred between one phase and another, but these were not substantial transformations.

**The House of the Lyre-Player**
The House of the Lyre-Player and the economic activities connected to it have been related to Lucius Popidius Secundus and his family, who was amongst the most politically active men in the years after the earthquake.

*Atrium (6)*
The *atrium* is entered from the Via di Stabia through a long corridor (3) which is divided into fauces and vestibule; a doorman positioned in room 5 would have controlled access. The *impluvium*, which occupies the cen-

tre of the long and narrow *atrium*, was stripped of its marble in antiquity. Around the *atrium* area are a series of *cubicula* (bedrooms), which in the first phase were perfectly symmetrical. *Cubiculum* 11 still preserves its original decoration in first style. The wall decoration of the *atrium*, now almost completely lost, was of fourth style, while the floor is cocciopesto adorned with marble incrustations.

*Tablinum (14)*
In an earlier phase the *tablinum* was much larger, as can be seen from the pilasters formed by two huge blocks of Sarno stone embedded in the south end of the east wall of the *atrium*. The axial view

## Wall-decoration

The Romans, basing themselves on techniques developed in Greece and the eastern Mediterranean, evolved highly sophisticated systems of decorating floors, walls and ceilings. The basic purpose of all such decoration was to enhance the prestige of the area affected. There was always a range of different materials and qualities available, to suit every pocket, and to mark out the special areas of the house where the most important social encounters took place. The technique of fresco decoration was to paint onto a layer of recently applied, and therefore still damp, lime and marble dust plaster. Effectively this layer represented the work which could be done in a day. There were up to seven preparatory layers consisting of sand and lime, applied one by one to the dried wall (and using finer grains in each layer); these served both to level the uneven surface of the wall and to insulate the wall from damp. Often a layer of ceramic fragments can be found between the wall and the preparatory layers which were designed to limit the damage caused by damp. Usually before applying the last layer the most skilled painter would trace the basic outline of the decoration, which would then be filled in from the top to the bottom by the painters. Figured panels would be painted last. The wall-paintings of Pompeii have an enormous importance for the history of ancient art since on the one hand they give us a glance at what must have been the great pictures of the Greek world, and on the other they permit us to understand the basis of

| | | |
|---|---|---|
| Late 3rd-early 1st c. BC | First style or 'structural' style | Architectural elements in relief, made from stucco and finished to look like marble. |
| 1st c. BC | Second style or 'architectural' style | Architectural prospectives, walls divided into socle (bottom), middle (with three-part division by columns and pilasters) and upper parts. |
| Late 1st c. BC-early 1st c. AD | Third style or 'ornamental' style | Same scheme as second style, elegant architecture, large mythical pictures, Egyptianising decorative elements. |
| Early 1st c. AD onwards | Fourth style or 'fantastic' style | Unreal architecture, exaggerated decoration mixing pictures and stucco reliefs. |

which cultural processes and which interpretations arrived in Italy. In effect, what we see at Pompeii is none other than Greek art mutated at Pompeii through Rome, and therefore not more than a pale reflection.

In 1882 August Mau wrote the first scientific work on ancient wall-painting, in which he attempted for the first time to categorise the wall-decoration of Pompeii. Thanks to his reflections and to subsequent studies, today Roman wall-paintings up to AD79 are categorised into four decorative systems, improperly called 'styles'.
- False marble ('first style'). The plaster is shaped and coloured to resemble rectangular panels of coloured marble. Typical of second and early first centuries BC, but may occur later.
- Architectural perspectives ('second style'). False perspectives of columns and architectural vistas receding into the distance are met in all 'styles' except the first. Characteristic of the decoration of the mid first century BC is that such false perspectives, often combined with false marble panels, occupy the entire field and the columns are large and dominate the foreground.
- Ornate framework ('third style'). Rich but delicate ornament characterises the taste of the reign of Augustus and the first half of the first century AD. Fine columns or candelabra form frames for central panel paintings, often with scenes from Greek mythology. Borders are worked in rich detail with lotus flowers and coloured patterns. Floral ornament, miniature heads and masks, and Egyptianizing elements are common. Garden scenes are worked with much botanical precision.
- Elaborate framework ('fourth style'). Decoration of the second half of the first century AD is the commonest found in Pompeii, and also the most varied. Many elements, including use of architectural perspective and framed mythological scenes, are shared with earlier styles. There is a wide range from very simple to very elaborate systems. One tell-tale sign is the use of repetitive patterned borders in a single colour ('embroidery borders') that could be applied by stencil.
[S.C.N.]

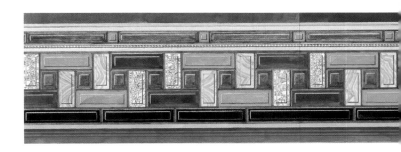

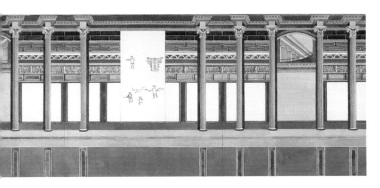

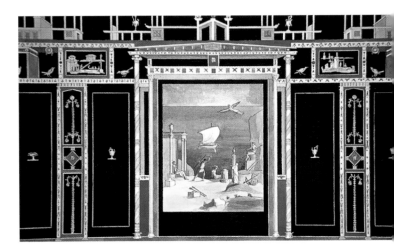

*33-36.*
*From top:*
*First style*
*Second style*
*Third style*
*Fourth style*

which one received when entering the house would have been stunning - through the *tablinum* one would have seen the two peristyles (17 and 32) divided by a window and in the background large rooms decorated with artistic reliefs. The resizing of the *tablinum*, due probably to structural reasons, created two asymmetrical *alae* (12 and 13). On the walls of *ala* 13 the preparations for a wall-painting can still be seen in a thick layer of cocciopesto-rich cement, designed to prevent damp, marked by many incisions which were made to aid the adhesion of successive layers. To the west, tables supported the busts of people connected to the house.

### Baths (38-43)
The baths were not functioning at the moment of the eruption of AD79 because they had been damaged previously by an earthquake. Their layout is canonical, with *apodyterium* (38), *tepidarium* (40), *calidarium* (41), and, to one side, the hypocaust which heated the rooms. From the baths the entrance to the middle peristyle was through a small tetrastyle *atrium*. The east wall of the *calidarium* is apsidal and the floor has a black and white geometric mosaic. The fresco on the walls portrayed an imaginary garden framed by a wooden fence.

*37. Detail of a capital of one of the columns in the lower peristyle (32) in the House of the Lyre-Player*

### Middle Peristyle (17)
The middle peristyle has six columns on its long sides and five on its short sides. The oldest columns are those made of rocks of grey tufa, whilst the newest are those made in *opus vittatum mixtum*. The columns supported an architrave decorated with painted landscapes and between the columns hung 'oscilla', marble plaques in the form of a shield decorated in relief on both sides. At the cente of the *viridarium* there is a semicircular basin around the borders of which bronze statues were discovered, including the group of dogs and boars, the deer, the lion and the serpent. In AD79 the large rectangular basin was covered with earth. The walls of the portico were decorated in fourth style painting, while the floors are made from crushed pieces of marble livened up with pieces of polichrome marble.

### Lower Peristyle (32)
The peristyle has five columns on its short sides and seven on its long sides, whose capitals were decorated with alternate palms and lotus flowers on a ribbon of plaster. It is on these columns that several graffiti were found which relate to Lucius Popidius Secondus, who was probably the owner of the house. We know nothing about the decoration of the walls of the portico but the floors are cocciopesto. The bases of the columns are covered with cocciopesto adorned with white *tesserae*.

### Exedra (35)
The large exedra was richly decorated in fourth style paintings with large mythological panels. To the east an episode in the story of Iphegenia in Tauris was portrayed: on the left Orestes, accompanied by his friend Pylades, is about to be sacrificed, in the background Iphegenia the priestess can be made out, attempting to save her brother, and to the right the king, Thoas, who wants to respect the law. On the south wall, Dionysius is dipicted discovering Ariadne, daughter of Minos, abandoned at Naxos by Theseus. Nothing is known of the painting on the north wall. The floor had a black and white geometric mosaic with a wide border decorated with a continuous meander.

### Oecus (21)
The large oecus functioned both as a large living room and a rest room. From here one passes through a corridor (25) into the service quarter with stable, to various cubicula (22, 23, 66), to a dining room (30) and into the storeroom (24). The oecus was adorned with a splendid third style wall-painting on the north wall which portrayed the Judgement of Paris: the Trojan hero sits to the right and, assisted by Hermes, judges which of the goddesses standing before him is the most beautiful, Hera, Aphrodite, or Athena.

### Cubiculum (20)
The *cubiculum* was decorated in third style wall-paintings with large mythological panels, which were removed and today can be seen in the National Archaeological Museum of Naples. On the east wall was a painting which has been interpreted in different ways: for some it represents Apollo and Poseidon at the court of Laomedon, first king of Troy, for others it portrays Achilles and Phoenix who heal the Greek hero Telephus of an in-

fected wound. The picture on the south wall represented the myth of Leda and the swan, and that on the north wall the love between Mars and Venus.

## Triclinium (19)

This is the largest room in the house and one of the largest in all Pompeii. It was completely covered in fresco paintings of the third style, of which only small pieces remain. A large part of a panel from the centre of the south wall is today to be found in the Naples Museum and represents the myth of Antiope. Antiope was a Maenad condemned to madness for having killed Dirce. The picture shows her sleeping while being guarded by Phocus who later will marry her. Nothing survives of the other walls. The floor has a black and white geometric mosaic with black borders.

## Upper Peristyle (56)

The peristyle has four tall and possessing columns on its short sides and six on its long sides. It was constructed when house 25 expanded at the expense of the house immediately to the east. Before this, there had been

a *tablinum* and a small garden in its place. A room which functioned as a *tablinum* (58) was constructed on the east side and flanked by two *cubicula*, and on the west side a large *biclinium* (bed with two couches) was built. When the House of the Lyre-Player also engulfed the house at no.28, the two were connected by means of a wide brick stairway to the west of the south wall. In the same period the western colonnade was closed in order to make a covered gallery in front of the *biclinium* which was decorated with an elegant fourth style painting.

## Atrium (47)

The *atrium* is built in *opus Africanum*, evidence that it belonged to a house built between the end of the third and beginning of the second centuries BC.
To this are adjoined a series of symmetrical rooms, subsequently transformed both in form and use. At the centre of the south side a stairway led to the rooms of the upper floor.
The south wall still preserves the wide opening of the

*tablinum* which was later demolished. The east *ala* (54) had a polichrome mosaic of the head of Medusa on its floor, which today can be seen in the Naples Museum. Basins were inserted into the west *ala*. The *impluvium* was bordered by a mosaic depicting the prows of ships, unfortunately not preserved today.

## Service quarter with stable (entrance no.28)

The House of the Lyre-Player increased its size after the earthquake of AD62/3 when it acquired the small house at no.28 and transformed it into a service quarter and stable equipped with an upper floor reached from room 21.
The marble head of a female portrait was found here. Before the transformation, the area had been a small house with a courtyard which was probably roofless like many other examples in Region I. In the rear a two-wheeled cart and four small rooms for horses were found. Probably the front of this house extended over part of the pavement in the period after AD63.
[S.C.N.]

## Floors

The most common flooring is cocciopesto, made from small fragments of amphorae and tiles secured with mortar and sometimes covered with a red glaze. At Pompeii there is also a more economical local version, which substitutes fragments of lava for the tiles and amphorae, and consequently is called 'lavapesto'. In some cases these pavements are decorated with marble *tesserae* placed in geometric patterns or regular points. Mosaic pavements are made from small truncated pyramids of stone, glass-paste or most commonly marble. These *tesserae* are fixed onto a layer of cement-like material and positioned in such a way to achieve a perfectly smooth level and to evoke the appearance of a carpet rather than a floor. The simplest mosaic, *opus tessellatum*, has above all geometric motifs and is made from quite large *tesserae*. The most elaborate, *opus vermiculatum*, has true pictorial scenes and is instead made from *tesserae* often less than 1mm². These pictures are positioned generally at the centre of the floor and are called 'emblems'. Finally, *opus sectile*, although not a real mosaic, is composed from polichrome marble usually in place of a pictorial scene and was used as an emblem. [S.C.N.]

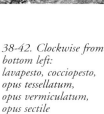

*38-42. Clockwise from bottom left: lavapesto, cocciopesto, opus tessellatum, opus vermiculatum, opus sectile*

# REGION I, INSULA 8
# THE SPANISH PROJECT

## Excavation in the House of the Indian Statuette (I.8.5)

The house owes its name to an ivory statue representing the Indian goddess Laksmi which was discovered during the excavations conducted by Maiuri in 1938-9. The façade of this house had been known since 1912 when Spinazzola excavated along the Via del-l'Abbondanza. The archaeological excavations undertaken by the Spanish team, sponsored by the Instituto del Patrimonio Histórico Español (MEC), were ostensibly based upon the hypothesis set out in the Rivista di Studi Pompeiani (1991-1992), in which it was suggested that, in the earliest phase of construction, the houses I.8.9/9, I.8.10 and I.8.5 had formed part of a single domestic structure. This hypothesis, previously derived from the analysis of the decoration, the paintings and pavements, permitted a reconsideration of the criteria by which land was divided into plots in the north end of the *insula* (I.8.) between the second century BC and the first century AD, and demonstrated that the system of division of urban land on an axis from north to south, at least in this *insula*, did not develop in the manner in which

it has been thought traditionally. In other words, the three architectural entities mentioned were in origin part of a single large house with two *atria*, with a principal entrance situated on the Via del-l'Abbondanza and another secondary entrance in the side street between *Insulae* 8 and 9 of Region I.

The aims of our excavation centred on two aspects: to identify the moment of the first division of space in the house, and to establish the

chronology of its different architectural phases. The stratigraphy obtained so far is derived from the excavations conducted at the room 3 and in the *atrium*, and indicates that this part of the house was constructed in the first half of the second century BC, with *opus signinum* pavements associated with paintings of the first style. At this time, the *atrium* lacked an *impluvium*; the domestic structure was characterised by an open courtyard.

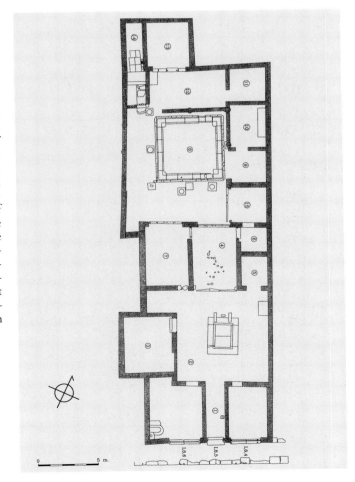

*43. Detail of the lararium in the 'Caupona' at I.8.8*

*44. Plan of the House of the Indian Statuette (I.8.5)*

From a structural point of view, the most important element discovered under the pavement of the *atrium* were two basins which the builders used to mix the mortar used for walls, paintings and pavements during large-scale changes which took place in the Tiberian-Claudian period: the level of the pavement of the *atrium* was raised considerably, connecting a complete system of drainage to the new *impluvium* - sloping slightly in respect to the axis of the house - which led to the cisterns located in the peristyle and to one of the shops on the Via dell'Abbondanza. Also, room 3 was created; in this initial phase it consisted of a wooden structure with tiles, which gave protection from the sun and from the rain in the large open courtyard.

In addition, the excavation illustrated that the dividing wall between room 3 of the house (I.8.5) and the *oecus* (3) of house I.8.8-9, traditionally thought to have been constructed in the first century AD, actually existed in the

first phase of the house during the second century BC. There were also deep and wide pits which broke the pavement of the large open court of the second century BC and which can be related, as in other parts of Pompeii, to the search for pozzolana.

The construction of the *atrium*, as we see it today, can be dated on the basis of particular forms of terra sigillata pottery to between the reigns of Tiberius and Claudius. This

chronology is corroborated by the new third style pavements and paintings.

The excavation of room 3 offers us material which dates to between the third and second centuries BC, with a lower limit between the years 90 - 80BC.

The pavement was raised after the construction of the pavement of the *atrium*, confirmed by a pre-existing small stairway connecting the old *opus signinum* of room 3 with this new pavement.

There was a curious inverse stratigraphy: the infill was composed of earth coming from an ancient rubbish dump, without any intrusion of contemporary material at the moment of its deposit.

*45. Detail of the excavation of the atrium in the House of the Indian Statuette*

*46. Detail of the foundation of the dividing wall between the shops and the atrium*

An excavation was carried out at the end of the peristyle (8), with the aim of understanding when the division took place with the inclusion of its columns into the dividing wall between the houses (I.8.5 and I.8.8-9). This too produced a surprising result: house I.8.8-9 had its original peristyle closed with a wall which was later destroyed in order to build the foundations of the peristyle of I.8.5. The traces of this wall can be seen in the stratigraphy. The architectural structure and the material enable us to date the construction between the reigns of Tiberius and Claudius; this construction affected the garden of the house I.8.8-9 which was reduced in width by several metres.

The results of the excavation and the previous study carried out in the whole of the house, allow us to confirm that the origin of the structure was in the middle of the second century BC and that its division took place between the reigns of Tiberius and Claudius. After the earthquake, special reinforcements were used in order to restore the affected places, although it is evident that during the course of three centuries small changes were made, manifest still in the walls, pavements and paintings.

[A.M.C., M.B.L., J.J.S.]

*47. Detail of the stratigraphy of the east side of the peristyle (8)*

*48. Detail of the excavation of the kitchen. A 'caccabus' (cooking-pot) in situ*

## House and 'Caupona' of Lucius Betutius Placidus (I.8.8-9)

The façade of this commercial establishment was first discovered in 1912 during the excavation of the Via dell'Abbondanza, but it was not until 1938 and 1939 that the excavation was completed. The results of these excavations remain to a large degree unpublished, and it has only been in the last few years that a Spanish team has begun to study these reports, and to compete the documentation of the 'Caupona' and its attached house.

The owner of the establishment at the moment of the eruption in AD79 appears to have been *Lucius Betutius Placidus*, since his name featured on different electoral manifestos painted on the façade (none of which are visible today) and on several amphorae found in the garden.

The structure surviving today is the result of a long process of evolution beginning in the first half of the second century BC, with successive rebuilding which culminated in the period after the earthquake of AD62/3. The building in its final phase had a rectangular plan with a surface area of 225 m², which followed the traditional layout of *atrium-tablinum*-garden, but which was preceded by a shop-front opening onto the Via dell'Abbondanza. The internal organisation of the property is dictated by two distinct entrances, one for the house and one for the shop.

The 'Caupona' or shop (1) consists of a counter with three branches covered in polichrome marble which contained a total of thirteen large vessels (*dolia*): these contained liquids and food for consumption. Inside one of these vessels,

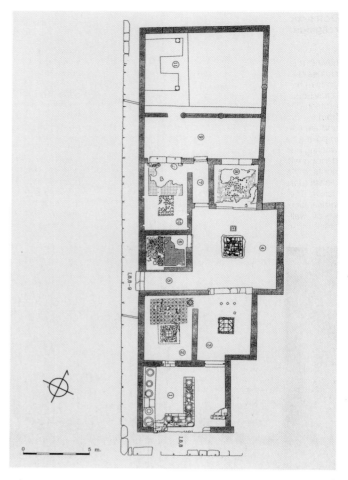

1611 coins were discovered, with a value equivalent to 683 sesterces, an amount which probably corresponds to the shop-takings of several days. Analysis of the textile fragments adhering to some of these coins revealed that they had been stored in a cloth or bag. On the rear wall there is a *lararium* in the form of a painted temple in fourth style, which has two Corinthian columns connecting the base to the triangular pediment. The *Genius* of the owner can be seen performing a libation on a portable tripod, flanked by the *lares* and by two divinities: Mercury, protector of com-

merce, and Bacchus, who, as god of wine, was the patron of *cauponae*, *tabernae*, and other places for the sale and consumption of drinks. Underneath this scene there is an altar with two serpents, symbols of the generator of fertility and potency, and a socle with a

*49. Plan of the House and 'Caupona' of Lucius Betutius Placidus*

*50. 'Caupona' and lararium*

## Domestic religious ritual

Many Pompeian houses have *lararia* - small shrines dedicated to the gods of that particular household. The *lares* protected the household from external threats, and are usually portrayed in pairs as young men wearing short tunics and dancing with drinking-horns (rhytons) and dishes (*paterae*) in their hands. The form of these *lararia* varies greatly, from simple wall-paintings to small wall-niches where miniature statues could be placed, to large shrines often set on podia and elaborately decorated.

Several different household gods were worshipped in these *lararia*. The *penates* were guardians of food-store, i.e. well-being of the family, while the *genius* represented the spirit of the head of the household (*paterfamilias*) and his family continuity. Sometimes Isis or Fortune are also found in *lararia* and symbolise abundance.

Snakes too were considered to be guardian spirits of the family, and were often portrayed on either side of the altar of the *lararium*. The *lararium* at I.8.8 illustrates all these different elements; it also has representations of Mercury and Bacchus, the gods of commerce and wine respectively. Domestic rituals at these *lararia* would be conducted by the *paterfamilias*, and would consist of regular small offerings of a portion of a meal and daily prayers to the different household gods, as well as special ceremonies such as betrothals, marriages, coming of age (when a boy would dedicate his *bulla* - a special pendant and the symbol of his boyhood - to the household gods). [J.B.]

and central pictures with birds and still-lifes. The niche in the west wall was a *lararium*. This *cubiculum* offers us the oldest decorative elements in the house: paintings of second style on the north and west walls, which survives under the main decoration, and a pavement of *opus signinum* which dates to the first century BC.

To the south of the *cubiculum* one enters the most important room of the house (10), which is open to the portico of the garden and communicates through a small gate with the passageway of the *atrium*. This room has third style decoration: on the east wall there are panels with a red background separated by architectural perspectives and a picture representing the rape of Europa. On the west wall there is a painting of Bellerophon as he tames Pegasus in the presence of Athena.

The rear part of the house is a garden. The portico (9) is decorated with still-life paintings on a white background which are best preserved on the east wall: a column with a herm of Priapus can be seen, in front of which three people are performing a sacrifice. To the right of this scene, although in a somewhat more deteriorated condition, one can identify clearly two figures and a goat. Originally this portico was L-shaped, but it lost its west side to the neighbouring Casa della Statuetta Indiana (I.8.5). The east side instead was used as a *triclinium* and one can still see the masonry beds and two brick columns covered in stucco which must have supported a pergula. A circular table and a dionisiac herm decorated the garden. There is evidence of a second storey, both from the original excavation documen-

black background decorated with plants and birds. During the restoration of this *lararium*, another, much older *lararium* was discovered underneath it. Situated to the right are the remains of a kitchen and the foundation of the stairway leading to an upper storey.

Several doorways connect the shop with the house, leading into a dining-room (*triclinium*) (2) with walls decorated in third style painting, and a

room (*oecus*) (3) connected to it, with a pavement of cocciopesto adorned with a central emblem made of marble sheets. The *oecus* gives passage into an undersized *atrium* (4), which has an *impluvium* covered with marble of several different varieties. The *atrium* can also be entered through a passageway (*fauces*) (5) from the street to the east. The *atrium*, which has a painted decoration called a 'overhanging socle', still contains part of a marble table and communicates with a bedroom (*cubiculum*) (6), with the reception room (*tablinum*) (7) and with the corridor (8) which leads into the garden (9). The *cubiculum* has a typical niche in the wall for the bed, and is decorated with a white background which is divided into panels decorated with garlands

*51. Third style wall-painting on the north wall of the cubiculum (6)*

*52. Pavement of the cubiculum (6)*

tation and from the drain on the external façade of the side-street which is constructed with amphorae and leads from a latrine on the upper floor into a cess-pit.

Besides the total of 1611 coins discovered in the shop, over a hundred objects were recovered from the excavations. These were distributed throughout the different rooms of the property with the exception of the *cubiculum* and the *tablinum*, which, according to the original reports, had been disturbed and therefore probably looted in an earlier period. The greatest proportion of artefacts (40.5%) are amphorae and other ceramic vessels, which relate to the activities of the shop. Given the quality of the wall decoration, above all of the *lararium* and the *triclinium*, as well as the pavements with *emblemata* in *opus sectile* and the garden with its summer *triclinium*, it is clear that *Lucius Betutius Placidus* had obtained a certain level of economic prosperity. Despite this, the dimensions of the house are modest, and there was an absence of jewellery and only a small number of bronze vessels (6.6%) and objects used for personal hygiene.

[A.M.C., J.J.S.]

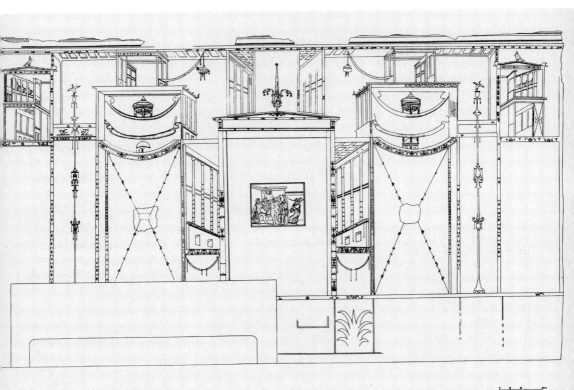

53. Third style wall-painting from the east wall of the triclinium (10)

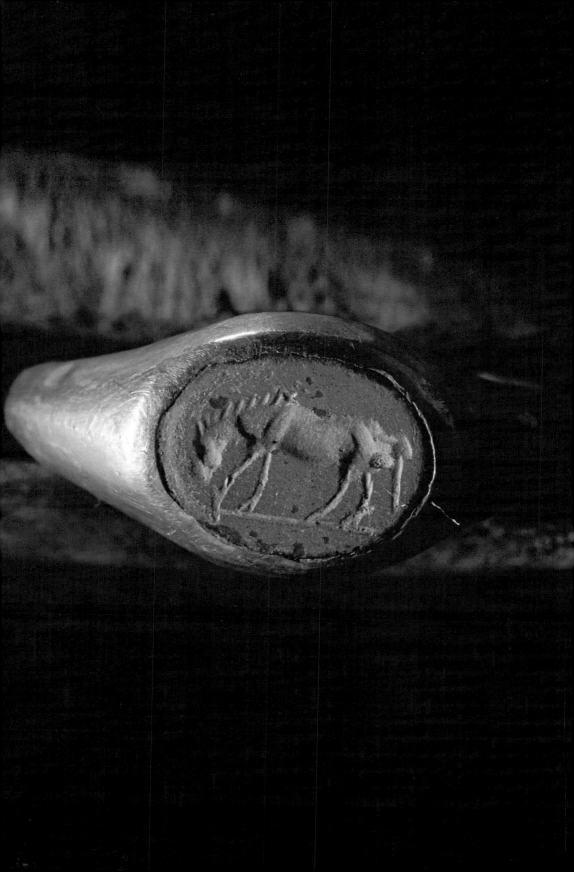

# REGION I, INSULA 9
# THE BRITISH PROJECT

## History

The houses in this *insula* as we see it go back at most two hundred years to the second century BC. But excavation at several points has shown that the area was inhabited as early as the sixth century BC, in the 'Etruscan' period of the city, and it is possible that even the present layout of the streets goes back to the same period. There are other traces of habitation in the fourth century and third century. But there was major rebuilding in the second century and first century, and little of the surviving decoration is earlier than the first century AD.

## Economy

The Via dell'Abbondanza is one of the most important streets of the town, and the heavy traffic made it ideal for shops. The houses that front on this street (1, 3, and 5) all have shops in their façades (2, 4, 6). The houses behind, which in each case link directly to the shops, show many signs of prosperity, in size, richness of decoration, and wealth of finds. Down the side-street, however, are much smaller properties, sparsely decorated, with numerous signs of craft activities (8, 9, 10). One (9) was a decorators' workshop. The land slopes downwards sharply from the main road, and the houses at the bottom (11, 12 and 13) show several signs of having become run-down by AD79. Nos.11 and 12, the House of Amarantus, functioned as a wine-shop in its final years. No.13, the House of the Ceres, is the only house in the *insula* to show no signs of commercial or craft activity; it is a private residence graciously decorated in the first century BC.

## House of the Beautiful *Impluvium* (I.9.1)

A substantial private residence, its main entrance (no.1) is now blocked by a concrete cast of the void left by its double wooden doors. A faded scene to the left of the door showing Mercury, god of trade, carrying a bag of money towards the door underlines the commercial origin of its prosperity. The finds from inside the house suggest that the inhabitants were still in AD79 fairly prosperous.

*54. Ring discovered during excavations in the atrium of the House of Amarantus*

*55. Plan of Insula I.9*

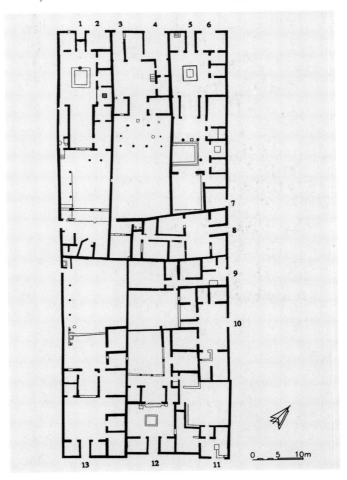

## Craft and trade

Evidence for a multitude of different craft and trade activities have been discovered all over Pompeii. Shops and workshops are commonly found in close vicinity (or even in direct relationship) with large and elaborately decorated houses, and it is clear from the tools and equipment discovered in many houses that craft activities could take place in the home as well as in the workshop.

Today, one of the clearest pictures of this wide-spread activity can be gleaned from Region I, since this was one of the last areas of the town to have been excavated. There is evidence of metal-working, lime-production, lamp and pot manufacture fulling, cloth-dying, wood-working, baking, garum production, and wine-production. Many, but not all, of these workshops are connected to shops, particularly along the Via dell'Abbondanza which was one of the main thoroughfares to the Forum. Some of these activities were famous throughout Italy. For example, the literary sources record that wines from Pompeii gave hangovers, and amphorae, bearing the names of two prominent Pompeian families, the Lassii and the Eumachii, have been found in large quantities in southern France.

*Amphorae*
Amphorae are large ceramic storage vessels in which goods were shipped around the Mediterranean. Mostly they were used to transport wine and olive oil, but many other contents have been documented. The overwhelming majority of amphorae discovered in Pompeii were made locally in Campania and most of these would have contained wine. However, other amphorae found in the town indicate that goods were imported into Pompeii from all over the Mediterranean area. For example, wine was imported from Greece (including Crete and Rhodes), and olive-oil

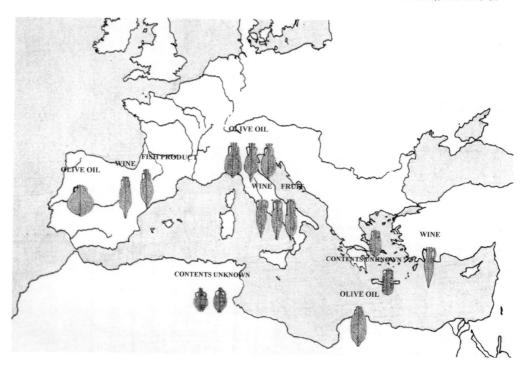

*56. Plan indicating the origins and contents of amphorae found in Pompeii*

the town travelled to farm plots of land outside the city walls.

*Spinning and weaving*
Wool-working was traditionally an important activity in Roman society, and is often a device used in the literary texts to illustrate the traditional morality of particular individuals. The evidence of spindles in Insula 9 suggests that spinning at least was a fairly common household craft activity in AD79. In contrast, although loom-weights are commonly discovered in the houses of Pompeii, they are only very rarely found in groups which would indicate a loom. Instead, their rather random distribution throughout different rooms of houses might suggest that in AD79 they were being used as door-stops. [J.B.]

was imported from North Africa (including Tripolitania) and Spain. Some of these amphorae can be identified as the produce of particular kiln sites in these countries, and others are labelled in Latin or Greek to indicate either their contents (such as a particular type of wine) or their final destination. While it is often possible to identify the original contents of amphorae, they probably had a wide range of secondary uses in the house such as water storage and transport. In Pompeii amphorae have been discovered which contained grain and lime.

*Tools*
A wide variety of different types of tool have been found in Pompeii, both plain and ornate,
including hammers, shears, spades and shovels, mattocks, hoes and axes, knives, sickles and scythes, forks, saws, and shears. Most would have been produced locally, even within the town itself, and would have seen extensive everyday use. A large proportion of these tools would have been used for general domestic work, such as basic repairs, gardening, and small-scale craft activities. The most common domestic tools in Insula 9 are knives, axes and picks. However, there are also tools with more specialised functions, such as chisels and mallets for wood-working, vices and tongs for metal-working, and hoes, rakes and scythes for agricultural work both within the city walls and
in the territory surrounding the town. Interestingly, many houses also contain fragmentary evidence of bridles and harnesses, and it seems possible that some residents of

*57. A selection of iron tools and a honing-stone*

*58. A ceramic loom-weight and he remains of several bone spindles*

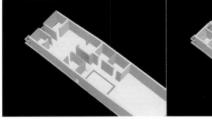
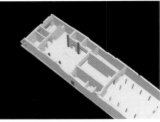

fume bottles, and tablewares in both ceramic finewares and bronze. The most striking content of the cupboard and chest was the hoard of 298 silver coins and three gold coins. We enter via its shop (no.2); excavated in 1913, few traces were recorded of the nature of its trade beyond brief mention of the discovery of fifteen knives, three *casseruole* (saucepans), a necklace of glass-paste beads, and a collection of bone 'pawns'.

### History of the house

The house as a whole passed through at least four major phases:

Phase 1. The original layout of the rooms around the *atrium*, seen in lava thresholds at a lower level goes back to the second century BC. Fragments of its early ('first style') decoration in false marbling

The main evidence for this prosperity can be seen in the remains of a wooden chest and an attached wooden cupboard which were found along the west wall of the *atrium* along with all their bronze, iron and bone fittings, and a bronze key. Inside the chest and the cupboard was a wide mixture of different artefacts, ranging from jewellery and personal items (a silver mirror, a silver jug, a silver crochet-hook, a gold ring and two gold bracelets) to lamps, glass per-

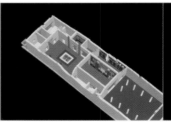

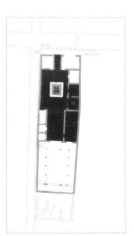
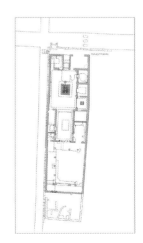

*59-62. 3D computer reconstruction of the four phases of development of the House of the Beautiful Impluvium*

are visible in side room (12).
Phase 2. The *atrium* area was remodelled, adding the rooms on its west. Four brick half-columns were built to support the roof beams above the *impluvium* (their stumps are visible). These changes may be dated to the late first century BC.
Phase 3. Major decoration

takes place in the early first century AD. The floors are raised and paved in mosaics and marble inlays. Walls are redecorated in the third style, including the *cubiculum* (11), the *tablinum* (7) and the *triclinium* (8/9).
Phase 4. Second half of first century AD, possibly after earthquake damage in AD

62/3. The brick half-columns are removed from the *atrium*, possibly leaving it unroofed. The *triclinium* is divided into a small room (9), with a new door to *ala* (10) and a smaller dining-room (8). A new kitchen is inserted in a previous bedroom (6), and the cellar below filled in. The failure to redecorate after any of these changes suggests that money was short, or the work still incomplete in AD79.

### Atrium (2)

The large *atrium*, which originally had a roof sloping inwards towards the centre, was handsomely re-paved in the mid-first century AD. The *impluvium*, which collected rainwater from the roof, was lined with pieces of coloured marble set in black mosaic; the marbles come from Africa, Greece, Turkey and Italy. A matching design is found at the threshold and in the centre of the long *tablinum*. The roof above the *atrium* was originally supported by four brick half-columns, visible in the floor; these were stripped out and plastered over, perhaps in a phase when the area was left unroofed.

A small room to the east of the entrance (12) has a patch of false marbling ('first style') from an earlier phase, probably the first.

The room (3) to the west of the entrance has a staircase

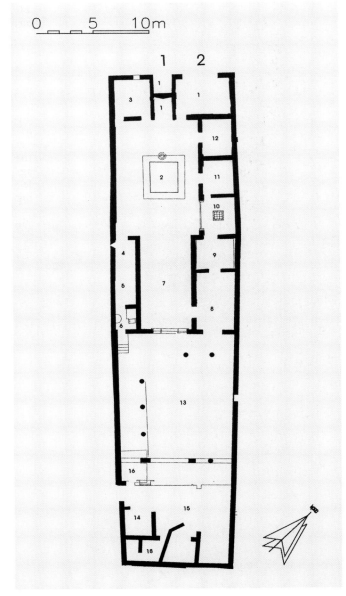

0    5    10m

*63. Plan of the House of the Beautiful Impluvium*

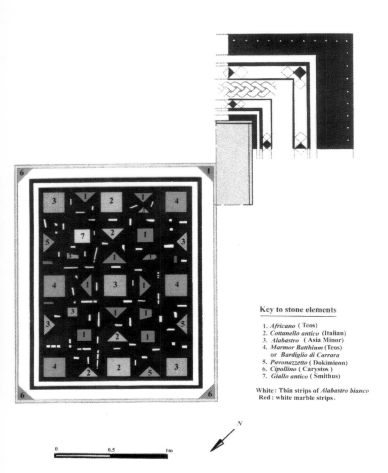

**Key to stone elements**

1. *Africano* ( Teos)
2. *Cottanello antico* (Italian)
3. *Alabastro* ( Asia Minor)
4. *Marmor Batthium* (Teos)
   or *Bardiglio di Carrara*
5. *Pavonazzetto* ( Dokimieon)
6. *Cipollino* ( Carystos )
7. *Giallo antico* ( Smithus)

White : Thin strips of *Alabastro bianco*
Red : white marble strips.

*64. Plan of the 'Beautiful Impluvium' indicating the different types of marble used in its decoration*

### Tablinum (7)

The *tablinum* was the traditional general reception space of the Roman house. Open to the *atrium* at one end, and to the peristyle garden at the other, this is unusually long. The east wall has fragments of an elaborate 'third-style' decoration of excellent execution: at the centre, a colonnade shown in perspective carries shields with portrait heads (*imagines clipeatae*), characteristic of aristocratic mansions, while at the sides porticoes frame the blue sky in a way that echoes the actual portico of the garden. In the west wall of the *tablinum* can be seen blocked-off doorways to two small rooms (5, 6); these have faded traces of decoration. They were subsequently blocked in and converted into a kitchen and service area. Below the later kitchen is a cellar; this must have been filled in when the kitchen was installed since its door is above the cellar steps. In the same area was originally a back door leading to the side street, subsequently blocked in.

### Triclinium (8/9)

The decoration of the long rectangular *triclinium* is far more fragmentary, but belongs to the same phase: against a black background are well-rendered architectural details, birds, and scenes depicting villas. This room was later divided in two by an unplastered wall; on either side of it can be seen the blocked-in recesses for the ends of the three couches which formed the traditional *triclinium* arrangement for dining (room 9). A black-and-white geometric mosaic at the centre of the couches collapsed into a void in the floor, but survives in fragments.

leading to rooms above the front of the house. The threshold is lower than the pavement of the *atrium*, and belongs to an earlier phase. The stairway originally opened directly on the *atrium*; this door was then blocked off.

Three rooms preserve decoration contemporary with the floors; the type of decoration ('third style') is normally dated to the first half of the first century AD.

### Cubiculum (11)

This small room served as a bedroom. The decoration in red panels framed by columns is typical of the 'third style' of the early first century AD. One well-preserved panel painting shows an erotic scene of a young woman embracing a tanned young man; his features are vaguely reminiscent of those of the emperor Augustus.

*Peristyle garden (13)*

The garden at the back is surrounded on three sides by the brick columns and pilasters of a peristyle. These are probably contemporary with the transformation of the *atrium* with its brick half-columns. At the bottom of the garden were originally rooms that opened directly on the portico; the brick pilasters that supported the floors can be seen in the cellar area below.

## House of the Fruit Orchard (I.9.5)

Similar to the House of the Beautiful *Impluvium* in layout and decoration, it enjoyed prosperity in the early first century AD, and most of what is visible dates to then. The entrance is blocked by a concrete cast of the doors, and access is through the shop at the side. The activity of the shop is not known, but it may have sold wine since the house in AD79 was full of amphorae (and in fact these far outnumber any of the other kinds of artefact found in this house). A rare bronze water-heater was discovered in the room directly off the shop which presumably would have been used to heat water to mix with wine; charcoal remains were found inside it, demonstrating that it was in use in AD79. Interestingly, there are also signs of ironworking in the back workshop.

*Atrium (2)*

The layout of the house follows the classic design of central *atrium*, *tablinum* open front and rear, leading to peristyle garden. The *atrium* was originally roofed, with central *impluvium*, serving to channel rainwater to the cistern below, accessible from a marble well-head. The walls were decorated with fine white plaster, and the floor paved with crushed lava patterned with white chips of marble. Stairs led from room (3) to upper rooms above the front and, from the corridor to the side of the *tablinum* (4), where the marks of the stairs are clearly visible, to rooms above the back.

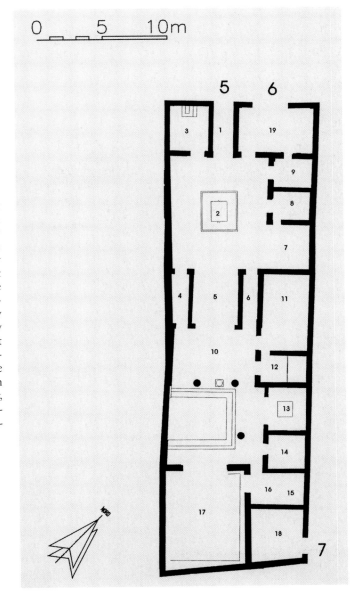

65. *Plan of the House of the Fruit Orchard*

## Cubiculum (8)

The *cubiculum* to the east of the *atrium* has a floor inlaid with marble chips that mark off the area for the bed at the end. The front part has a geometrical mosaic carpet. The walls are decorated with gardens scenes against a sky-blue background, showing flowering shrubs behind a low terrace, statues, fountains and decorative plaques, and a rich bird-life. Many motifs are drawn from Egyptian religion (e.g. the Apis bull) and reflect the popularity of such themes after the conquest of Egypt. The precise drawing of flora and fauna is typical of the early first century AD (compare the Villa of Livia near Rome).

## Cubiculum (12)

A *cubiculum* with mosaic floor has a raised dais for a wide bed. The walls are decorated with garden scenes like those of the other *cubiculum*, but with a black background. On the end-wall, a snake is shown sliding up a fig-tree. A window in the south wall opening on the garden has been blocked off.

## Triclinium (11)

The *triclinium*, linked by a door to the *cubiculum* (two-room suites were common), has a background decoration of the same (early first century AD) date. Delicately painted architectural structures divide off three panels above the space for the three couches of the *triclinium*. Mythological scenes represent in narrative style Diana observed bathing by Actaeon (west), the Seven against Thebes (north), and the fall of Icarus (east). A collection of good quality bronze and ceramic

66. *3D computer reconstruction of the cubiculum (12)*

67. *3D computer reconstruction of the triclinium (11)*

## Kitchen

The size, location and equipment of kitchens in Pompeii vary from house to house, and, in fact, there are some houses with no obvious place for food preparation, and it is likely that cooking in these houses took place on small portable braziers in the atrium or garden areas. However, in general terms, many kitchens have fixed masonry podiums, which are often tiled. Many of these podiums have arched niches underneath the main tiled surface in which wood for cooking could be stored. Cooking took place on the surface of the podium: iron tripods or amphorae points would be used to support cauldrons, pots and pans above a small fire. In contrast, built-in ovens are very rare, reflecting the fact that much food was boiled rather than baked. In the House of Ceres (I.9.13) cooking pots (along with a collection of other household objects) were stored in a small chest by the side of the podium, although it is quite normal to find cooking vessels stored in many different rooms of the houses. [J.B.]

*68. A selection of kitchen artefacts from the House of Ceres*

## *Triclinia* and dining

It is clear that banquets and dinner-parties were an important part of Roman social life and social status.

In Pompeii, dining-rooms are often one of the most elaborately decorated spaces in the house. Banquets could take place either inside the house or in the garden, and many Pompeian houses have permanent garden *triclinia* (usually consisting of three connected couches) for use in the summer months. The standard arrangement of three couches at the end of a long rectangular room reflected Roman social rituals and there was a strict seating plan reflecting social status. Dinner (*cena*) would start around 4pm and last well into the evening, and might be accompanied by entertainment of different forms, such as readings and recitations, lyre-players, singers, dancers, acrobats, and clowns.

Lighting would be provided by bronze and ceramic lamps, sometimes placed on elegantly decorated candelabra. Occasionally, lanterns have also been discovered.

Even the smallest houses usually have a small number of specific table vessels, which suggests that formal dining had a role to play in the everyday life of even poor inhabitants of the town.

In general throughout the town there is a wide variety of both forms and materials of these vessels which illustrate the importance of this activity. A large proportion of the dinner service consisted of bowls, basins and jugs, which reflects the nature of the meal. There was no cutlery as we would expect, with the exception of spoons for eating shell-fish and eggs. Instead, diners would help themselves from dishes by placing food onto a plate or bowl with the left hand and eating with the fingers of the right. The food would be cut into small pieces by slaves before being served to the diners. Water-jugs and basins therefore served to wash sticky fingers during the course of the meal.

Wine would also be served, although this was mixed with water and, in the winter months, warmed up. One such water/wine heater was discovered in the House of the Fruit Orchard (I.9.5).
[J.B.]

*69. A selection of tablewares from Insula I.9*

*70. A candelabrum discovered in the House of the Fruit Orchard*

tablewares were found distributed throughout the house, along with a decorated candelabrum.

## Peristyle garden (10)

A colonnade surrounds on three sides a small garden. On the east wall, a slab of Egyptian obsidian is set between the doors to the two principal rooms, whether as a mirror, or a talisman. In AD79 the garden was used to store amphorae.

*71. The peristyle of the House of the Fruit Orchard in 1952*

## Room (13)

A small room south of the *cubiculum* shows signs of repeated remodelling. We can see four phases.

First phase (c.100 BC). The rear wall is decorated in false marble panelling (first style); there is no upper room, and perhaps no division between rooms 12 and 13 in this phase. Second phase (first half of first century AD). The adjoining room (12) is remodelled and decorated with scenes of a garden. A window is opened in the wall, allowing a view from the bed through room 13 into the real garden. Beams are inserted into the wall to carry an upper floor.

Third phase (second half of first century AD). The room is remodelled: the pavement is raised with a marble threshold and an inlaid marble floor

pattern. A frame is inserted around the opening to the garden to carry a wide wooden door.

Last phase (after AD62). The doorway is further narrowed, the window is blocked, and the walls are replastered.

## Cubiculum (14)

A further bedroom to the south has a geometric pattern of marble chips in its floor. A similar, but much more complex pattern, no badly damaged, covered the floor of the large room south of the peristyle.

## Service area (15/16)

Hidden in the south-east corner is the service area, a stairway up, and a latrine under the stairs, and at a lower level, a workshop with a separate backdoor.

House no. 8 contained many finds of low value, including an exceptional number of lamps (36). Many of the lamps used in the town were produced locally (although there is some evidence of imported lamps). A workshop producing lamps and small ceramic pots was uncovered in Region I (I.20.2). Here a large furnace was found and a series of different matrices for making the lamps, two of which are displayed in the exhibition. Each matrix varies to differing degrees in shape and decoration, which emphasises the range of the choices available to the inhabitants of Pompeii.

House no.9 seems to have been a painters' workshop, to judge by the numerous small pots of pigment. There were over 100 of these small pots,

## Houses I.9.8-9: Craft activity in the side street

The side street to the east of *Insula* 9 has a very different feel to the main road. The road itself is unpaved, and the pavements are poorly made. The four doors that open on the road lead to premises without any pretensions to grandeur or elegance. Walls are only rarely decorated with more than plain plaster, and floors are mostly of beaten earth or simple cocciopesto. Construction of the façades retains the original build of *opus Africanum* framework in Sarno stone; there are few signs of major investment in reconstruction, though numerous minor modifications have taken place.

There are abundant signs of craft activity in the area. Door no.7, which forms part of the House of the Fruit Orchard, leads to a workshop. Finds of iron slag point to iron working, though there is no trace of a furnace for a smithy.

72. A selection of lamps found in house I.9.8, and two matrices from the nearby workshop at I.20.2

73. Some of the 'paint-pots' from House I.9.9

most of which were stored in a wooden cupboard near the entrance to the house, and which contained pigments of many different colours (shades of red, orange, brown, black, blue, white, and green). Several grinding-stones and a pestle were found with the pots, and many of the pigments had already ground down into fine powders which could then be mixed to make paint. In addition, there was a collection of different tools, including compasses and a plumb-bob which would have been used to design and execute paintings on a wall, and spoons and spatulas which were used to mix the pigments.
[A.W.H.]

## The House and Bar of Amarantus (I.9.11-12)

Houses I.9.11 and 12, first uncovered in 1952-1953, but then effectively abandoned, offered a valuable opportunity for testing out existing ideas about their history. The absence of pavements of any kind in the *atrium* of House 12 and the 'garden' of House 11 offered the advantage of larger areas to excavate below the AD79 surface in order to understand better their earlier histories. Excavation to the geological subsoil would have the potential of revealing evidence of occupation earlier than the construction of either of the two houses.

The complex consists of two units, which seem to have been connected throughout their development. Door no.11 leads directly to a masonry shop counter or bar, decorated with pieces of coloured marble; behind the bar are a couple of small service rooms, leading to a large garden area, partly surround-

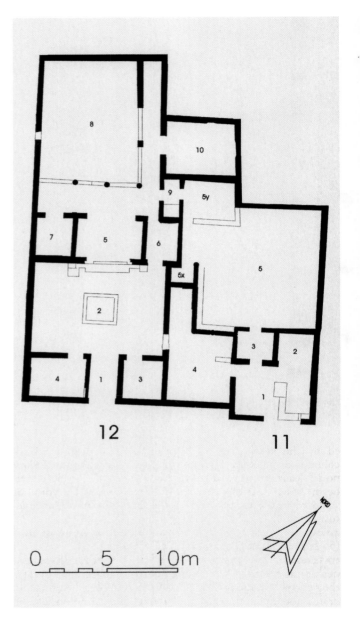

*74. Plan of the House and Bar of Amarantus*

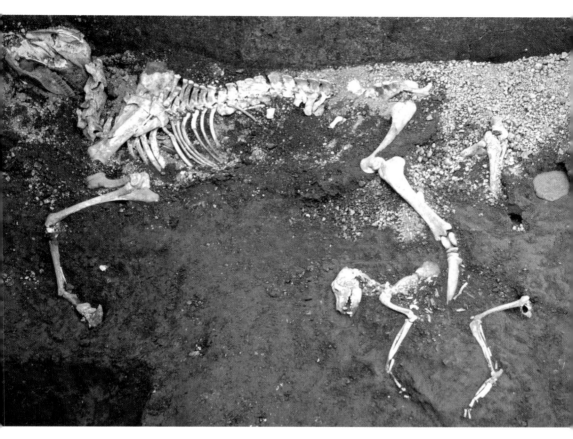

*75. Excavation of the skeletons of a donkey and a dog in the House of Amarantus, 1995*

ed by the blocked-in brick columns of a peristyle. Door no.12 leads to what should be the residential quarters, a standard arrangement of narrow entrance (*fauces*), central *atrium* (2), with a *tablinum* (5) beyond it, acting as the transition to the peristyle garden (8) at the back. Around the peristyle are the only decorated rooms of the house:

the *tablinum* itself, a *cubiculum* (7), and the *triclinium* (10). All three are decorated in the 'fourth style' typical of the final decades of the city.

## Condition of the house in AD79

Before commencing excavation below the AD79 surface it was possible to learn more about the condition of the two houses at the time of the eruption. Not all the volcanic material had been removed in the original excavation and further work in one room revealed that it had been used as a stable. The remains of a donkey with a dog at its feet were found collapsed against a manger in one of the front rooms of House 12.

In the *atrium* behind were the remains of amphorae which had carried wine from Crete, probably for sale at the bar in House 11. In the garden to the rear of the bar examination of the ink writing on empty amphorae revealed the name of the owner, SEXTUS POMPEIUS AMARANTUS. Pollen evidence told us much about the (poor) condition of the houses and stable at the time of the eruption. To give one example, the fodder or bedding for the donkey contained large amounts of walnut pollen.

## Date of construction of House 12

By conventional wisdom, the techniques and materials

*76. 1952 excavation*
*photograph of the*
*amphorae stored in*
*the atrium of the House*
*of Amarantus*

used in the building of House 12, such as the squared, ashlar blocks of Sarno stone (*opus quadratum*) making up the façade, and the framework construction in *opus Africanum* of the internal walls, suggested a history which might go back to the fourth century BC. Excavation of the entire *atrium* area throws the standard dating into question. While evidence of fourth century habitation is there, it belongs to layers far earlier than the foundation of the house walls as they stand. These cannot be earlier than the mid-to-late first century BC. Evi-

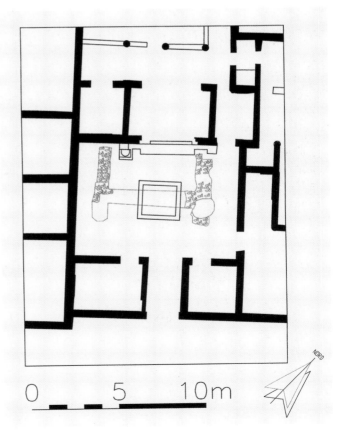

*77. Close-up of the graffito SEX. POMPEIUS AMARANTUS found on one of the amphorae*

*78. Plan of the sixth century BC structure under the House of Amarantus*

dence for this is provided by the presence of particular types of pottery, such as the red, glossy, Italian sigillata (tablewares), which replace the black, Campanian tablewares, and become established in the second half of the first century BC.

But though excavation contradicted the apparently early date of the walls that stand, it demonstrated, equally surprisingly, that occupation of the area goes back far earlier that predicted by the usual chronology of expansion of the city. Pottery dating back to the sixth century is found extensively, including a fragment in Etruscan lettering bearing the end of an Etruscan personal name. Foundation trenches filled with pieces of lava provide evidence of a rectilinear building on the same alignment as the Roman street grid as early as the mid-sixth century BC. This is the first structure of this date to be excavated in Pompeii and it raises the important question of the origin of the city and its street plan. Although it is generally believed that the archaic city was confined to the south-western (Altstadt) quarter, the evidence from House 12 argues for a more comprehensive archaic plan, possibly of Etruscan origin.

## History of construction of House 11

In contrast, the evidence of numerous alterations to the fabric of House 11, which is built largely of mortared rubble, suggested a complicated history of change to its internal space. Here, excavation below the AD79 levels allows a better understanding of the

*79. A sherd of sixth century pottery incised with the Etruscan personal name ...ARESA*

*80. Clockwise from top right: grape pips, fig pips, fish bones, sea urchin shell*

## Food and diet in Pompeii as revealed by the excavations of I.9.11/12

The cookery book of Apicius, which gives recipes for such dishes as flamingo with coriander and dormouse on a stick, and the Satyricon of Petronius, in which Trimalchio serves his guests hare with sow's udders, have given a rather unbalanced popular view of Roman diet. Wall paintings at Pompeii also tend to emphasise the luxurious aspect of the diet, depicting bowls of fruit and game hanging in the larder. This is not to say everyday food was monotonous - soil samples sieved from the excavation have given evidence of a very varied diet. Bones and shells survive in the soil and plant remains were preserved either by being carbonised in fires or mineralised in latrines. There are three main sources of food remains: waste from food preparations, the contents of latrines and burnt offerings of food. Some crop cleaning occurred on the site during the early phases, giving rise to burnt chaff of emmer wheat, grains of six-row hulled barley, common millet, foxtail millet and seeds of field bean.

During the later phases, the waste was mostly from kitchen and table. Charred olive stones were numerous but walnut shell fragments and a peach stone were also found. There were bones of domestic mammals, such as sheep, pig and cattle, while wild birds were caught including song thrush and blackbird. Marine resources were exploited, with bones from fishes of various sizes and a particularly wide range of shellfish was found including scallop, murex, limpet, wedge shell, cockle, sea urchin, cuttlefish and spiny lobster.

The remains from latrines had passed through the human gut and included cereal bran, seeds of cornfield weeds, such as catchfly (Silene gallica), numerous fig pips, rather fewer grape pips and some probable cucumber seeds. Also swallowed were small fish bones, perhaps from garum (fish sauce), scales from larger fish and songbird bones. The sacrificial/burnt offerings gave a new insight into diet for fruits and nuts were burnt intact. There was a veritable cornucopia of offerings, particularly figs, grapes and pine nuts but also hazel nuts, dates, lentils and common millet. The only prepared food found was bread with opium poppy seeds pressed into the crust. Sheep, goat and many cockerels were sacrificed. They were mostly represented by heads and feet, the remainder of each animal probably being butchered and eaten.

Thus the occupants of Houses 11 and 12 can be seen to have enjoyed what in many aspects is still a familiar Mediterranean diet bringing together the products of garden, orchard, field pasture and sea, even if the occasional limpet did have to be endured. [M.R.]

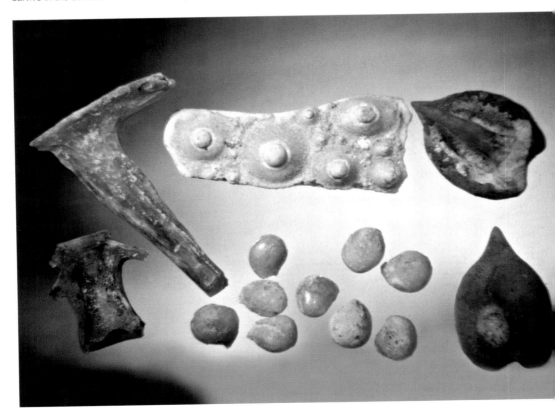

significance of changes evident in the upstanding walls. Excavation at the front of the house shows the complexity of these changes. In the case of the bar counter it is clear that this was only constructed in the last decade or two before the eruption. This reminds us that any particular function associated with a house as it was in AD79 may have been short-lived.

## Exploration of the garden of House 11

In AD79 the garden area (5) was used for storing empty amphorae from the bar. But it was also possible to demonstrate by taking casts of root cavities that a variety of plants were growing there, including some vines and one well-established tree. However, it was evident that this final garden surface was about half a metre above the level presupposed by the brick columns of the peristyle. Deeper excavation into and below the garden of House 11 revealed important evidence of domestic sacrifice.

Careful examination of the contents of a cist which was constructed early in the first century AD showed that it had been used to contain the cremated remains of at least three lambs and seventeen mature cockerels represented by the remains of the less edible parts, such as skull, wing and limb bone fragments. Associated with these bones were the charred remains of stone-pine nuts, figs and dates. The character of this assemblage suggests the careful interment of the remains of household sacrifice, perhaps over a number of years until the final burial of the cist by the dumping of soil to create the garden in the mid-first century AD.

At lower levels, numerous other features emerged, particularly a series of demolished walls indicating previous structures beneath the garden, several cess-pits linked to latrines of the first century AD, and a series of other pits dug to recover building sand for the construction of mortared walls. These pits were exceptionally rich in finds (broken vessels, lamps, loom-weights etc), and in organic materials revealing the changing diet of the inhabitants.

[M.G.F.]

# APPENDIX: MODEL AND DEVELOPMENT
# OF AN ADAPTIVE HYPERMEDIA SYSTEM

The development of a model and a hypermedia application differs in several critical ways from any other type of software; in order to develop this type of software, one needs a constructive interaction between different professionals with different specialities and to organise it in such a way as to make it accessible and easy to utilise by users. To this must be added an open hypermedia system, distributed and adaptive, which is accessible by means of the WWW (World-Wide Web).

Such an application has been developed for *Insulae* 4, 8, and 9 of Region I of Pompeii, and in more detail for particular houses such as the House of the Lyre-Player.

The work developed in two phases: the first phase was dedicated to the creation of the model of the data, that is a collection of logical objects which give an abstraction of the real world. Much scientific work is invested in this phase, and it has a fundamental role as a point of reference for the successive development of the application.

The model of the data was organised according to a hierarchical structure of region - *insula* - house - room - wall - context, then elaborated in such a way to support the construction of imaginary models. This has several objectives:

- to increase the local coherence of each source of information, indicating the semantic relationships between them and diminishing the impression of fragmentation of the data;

- to increase the global coherence, by using indexes and references at a more abstract logical levels;

- to aid the orientation of the user by providing indications of his/her correct position and of the way in which other information can be reached;

- to simplify the navigation, making it adaptive to all users at the level of the interface.

The second phase was dedicated to the development of the hypermedia application. The software used was primarily Dynamic HTML, Java and Javascript, which respond well to the problems of dynamics, easy access and distribution needed by the model of the data. Such a choice allows the hypermedia application to be used on both local and geographical networks.

As a counterpart to such versatility, it it necessary to deal with numerous other problems of a technical as well as cognitive nature.

One of these has been the choice of the format and fragmentation of the information, which are crucial factors in the transmission of data: fundamental to this aim has been a careful analysis of the subject, composed of traditional media such as images and text, to a conspicuous series of maps and drawings of walls. For this, a vectorial format has been used which has allowed the information to be compressed, a good vision of the whole to be created, and direct navigation on maps, walls and pavements to be possible. The adaptability of the model is especially clear at the level of the application above all in the possibility it offers the user to choose the most appropriate interface for his or her cognitive model (for example, the user can decide how to view the forms or the designs of the single walls).

At the end, access to the model is independent of the hardware and software used to create the programme.

[A.D., W.B.]

*81. Pits and a cist in the garden of House 11*

**THE ERUPTION OF AD79**
Sigurdsson, H., Cashdollar, S. and Sparks, S.R.J. (1982) *The eruption of Vesuvius in AD79: reconstruction from historical and volcanological evidence.* "Archaeological Journal of America" 86:39-51.

**THE EXCAVATIONS**
De Carolis, E. (1990) *Gli sviluppi dell'archeologia pompeiana: 1748-1900.* In: *Fotografia a Pompei nell'800 dalle collezioni del Museo Alinari*: 11-20. Soprintendenza Archeologica di Pompei. Florence.

Fiorelli, G. (1875) *Descrizione di Pompei*: 61-68. Naples.

Maiuri, A. (1950b) *Gli Scavi di Pompei dal 1879 al 1948.* In: *Pompeiana. Raccolta di studi per il secondo centenario degli scavi di Pompei*: 9-40. Naples.

**BUILDING TECHNIQUES**
Adam, J-P. (1984) *La construction romaine. Matériaux et techniques.* Paris.

**URBAN DEVELOPMENT**
De Caro, S. (1991-2) *La città sannitica: urbanistica ed architettura.* In: Fausto Zevi (ed.), *Pompei*, I-II, Vol I:23-46. Naples.

Maiuri, A. (1973) *Alla ricerca di Pompei preromana: saggi stratigrafici.* Naples.

Ward-Perkins, J.B. (1984) *Note di topografia e urbanistica.* In: F. Zevi (ed.), *Pompei 79. Raccolta di studi per il decimonono centenario dell'eruzione Vesuviana*: 25-39. Naples.

**HOUSES**
Castiglione Morelli del Franco, V. and Vitali, R. (1989) *L'insula 8 della Regio I: un campione d'indagine socio-economica.* "Rivista di Studi Pompeiani" III:185- 221.

D'Ambrosio, A. (1996) *Termopolio e Casa di L. Vetuzio*

*Placido in Pompei.* In: *Abitare sotto il Vesuvio*: 109-113. Ferrara.

De Vos, M. (1990) *Pompei. Pitture e Mosaici*, I:117-177.

Elia, O. (1937) *Le pitture della Casa del Citarista.* In: *Monumenti della pittura antica III. Pompei fasc.I.* Rome.

Fulford, M. and Wallace-Hadrill, A. (1995-6) *The house of Amarantus at Pompeii (I.9.11-12): an interim report on survey and excavations in 1995-6.* "Rivista di Studi Pompeiani" VII:77-113.

Fulford, M. and Wallace-Hadrill, A. (1998) *Unpeeling Pompeii.* "Antiquity" 72, no.275:128-145.

Guirál Pelegrín, C. et al. (1991-1992) *Missione archeologica spagnola a Pompei: la casa-caupona I,8,8-9 di L. Vetutius Placidus.* "Rivista di Studi Pompeiani" V:89-110.

Ling, R. (1997) *The Insula of the Menander.* Oxford.

Pesando, F. (1997) *"Domus" edilizia privata e società pompeiana fra III e I secolo a.C.*: 27-34. Rome.

Tella, F. (1989) *Un quadro con Bellerofonte e Atena dalla caupona I,8,8.* "Rivista di Studi Pompeiani" III:105-110.

Wallace-Hadrill, A.F. (1994) *Houses and society in Pompeii and Herculaneum.* Princeton.

**WORK AND COMMERCE**
Cerulli Irelli, G. (1977) *Una officina di lucerne fittili a Pompei.* In: M. Annecchino (ed.), *L'Instrumentum Domesticum di Ercolano e Pompei nella prima età imperiale*: 53-72. Rome.

**DAILY LIFE**
Berry, J. (1997) *The conditions of domestic life in Pompeii in AD79: a case-study of houses 11 and 12, Insula 9, Region I.* "Papers of the British School at Rome" LX: 103-125.

Etienne, R. (1986) *The day a city died.* (English trans 1992) London, New York.

**DOMESTIC ARTEFACTS**
Annecchino, M. (1977a) (ed.) *L'Instrumentum Domesticum di Ercolano e Pompei nella prima età imperiale.* Rome.

Berry, J. (1997) *Household artefacts: towards a reinterpretation of Roman domestic space.* In: R. Laurence and A. Wallace-Hadrill (eds.) *Domestic space in the Roman world: Pompeii and beyond.* "Journal of Roman Archaeology" Supplementary Series 22: 183-195.

Dwyer, E. (1982) *Pompeian Sculpture in its Domestic Context*: 79-108. Rome.

Morel, J-P. (1979) *La ceramica e il vetro.* In: F. Zevi (ed.), *Pompei 79. Raccolta di studi per il decimonono centenario dell'eruzione Vesuviana*: 241-264. Naples.

Pirzio Biroli Stefanelli, L. (1991) (ed.) *L'argento dei romani: il vasellame da tavola e d'apparato.* Rome.

Tassinari, S. (1993) *Il vasellame bronzeo di Pompei.* Rome.

**GENERAL**
Conticello, B. (1990) *Rediscovering Pompeii.* Rome.

Laurence, R. (1994) *Roman Pompeii: space and society.* London.

Ward-Perkins, J.P. and Claridge, A. (1976) *Pompeii AD79.* London.

Zanker, P. (1993) *Pompei. Società, immagini urbane e forme dell'abitare.* Turin.

Zevi, F. (1979) *Pompei 79. Raccolta di studi per il decimonono centenario dell'eruzione Vesuviana.* Naples.

## GRAPHIC AND PHOTOGRAPHIC SOURCES

cover, pp. 4-5; figs. 1, 4, 6-11;
p. 21; figs. 25-29, 33-36, 38-43,
55-70, 72-75, 77-81: British
School at Rome
cover; figs. 2, 3, 22, 23, 30-32,
37, 50, 71, 76: Archaeological
Superintendency of Pompeii
figs. 5, 44-49, 51-53: Spanish
School of History and
Archaeology at Rome
figs. 12-20: Dutch Institute
at Rome
fig. 21: Archaeological
Superintendency of Naples and
Caserta
fig. 54: Christopher Warde-Jones

**ILLUSTRATIONS**
pp. 4-5: Marie-Noelle Janssens
pp. 14-15: Ludovico Bisi
figs. 12-20: Hans Knikman
p. 21; fig. 56: Simone di Lauro
figs. 22, 23, 30, 31: Walter
Balzano, Vittorio Celentano,
Antonella Dandolo
cover; figs. 33-36: Nicholas
Wood
figs. 44, 49, 51-53: Elvira
González De Durana
figs. 55, 63, 65, 74, 78: Raphael
Helman, Marie-Noelle Janssens
figs. 59-62: Justin Snell, Raphael
Helman
fig. 64: William Clarke
figs. 66, 67: Justin Snell,
Raphael Helman, Nicholas
Wood

UNPEELING POMPEII

*Texts*
Andrew Wallace-Hadrill [A.W.H.]
Michael Fulford [M.G.F.]
Antonio Mostalac Carillo [A.M.]
José Luis Jiménez Salvador [J.J.S.]
C. Miguel Beltrán Lloris [M.B.L.]
Herman Geertman [H.G.]
Salvatore Ciro Nappo [S.C.N.]
Mark Robinson [M.R.]
Joanne Berry [J.B.]

Printed in 1998 on behalf of Elemond Spa
by Tipografica La Piramide, (Rome)